Readers, Writers, Relatives, and Friends Rave

ABOUT *RIDE, BABY, RIDE!*

"Sometimes you don't go looking to create your own destiny. It comes to find you. Leilani Hurles is a perfect example of someone having a destiny forced upon her. She did not ask for ovarian cancer, but it came. And then she decided that if dealing with it would be her destiny, it would be a hell of a ride! Her positive, humorous way of looking at life has carried her through fear, chemotherapy, and her mission to share her destiny by giving courage to others. Rather than learn how to suffer, Leilani has learned how to live! And in *Ride, Baby, Ride!* that lesson is apparent on every page."

— Patrick Snow, best-selling author of
Creating Your Own Destiny and *The Affluent Entrepreneur*

"The cancer experience is such an emotional and physical roller coaster. In *Ride, Baby, Ride!*, Leilani Hurles takes us on a ride filled with humor, grace, and her wonderfully positive spirit. I guarantee that people will laugh out loud at some of her stories as well as be moved by the poignancy of others. This book is a treasure."

— Nancy Tucker, President and CEO, CanCare, Inc.

"Coping with cancer is a feat few people can handle with an uplifting attitude. Leilani Hurles is the rare person who does more than cope—she lives life with an energetic passion as if cancer were just something to check off her list. Her determination and her desire to help others is a spirit every doctor wishes his patients to possess. I can testify that *Ride, Baby, Ride!* accurately portrays that spirit and the antics I have witnessed in Leilani throughout her cancer journey. She truly is a believer in life."

— Dr. Paul I. Cook MD., FACOG, Obstetrics and Gynecology

"If laughter truly is the best medicine, then Leilani has what it takes to survive cancer. I've had many patients, but few with her spirit, sense of humor, and determination not to give up. She credits me with saving her life, but her optimism was essential to get her through the process."

— Dr. Michael W. Bevers, M.D., Professor, Director,
Gynecologic Oncology Outreach Program, Department of
Gynecologic Oncology, MD Anderson Cancer Center

"Leilani Hurles, in her courageous walk through the dreaded disease of cancer, is inspiring to anyone who reads *Ride, Baby, Ride!* with its tidbits of wisdom and humor. Even in the face of scary tests, surgeries, and chemotherapy, her positive outlook and her reliance upon her God shows us an enlightened journey through life's many challenges. Leilani has a way of writing that adds humor to even the most difficult of experiences. So tell anyone you know who is dealing with cancer to read *Ride Baby, Ride!* for an uplifting and inspirational experience."

— Liah Holtzman, author of *Forgiveness Equals Fortune*

"It has been said that life is more interesting in the deep end of the pool. Leilani Hurles has been a swimmer all her life. But a couple of years ago, she found herself in really deep water. She could have drowned in her cancer, but she's learned some new ways to swim and in this book she teaches the strokes to us. She never stops being honest, hilarious and hopeful. If you want to learn to swim in deep water, read this book."

— Dave Peterson, Pastor, Memorial Drive Presbyterian Church

"Nothing you read about me in this book is true, or if it is, I don't remember it."

— Oved "Magoo" Essary, Leilani's Dad

"I'm a rabid fan of *Ride, Baby, Ride!* and Leilani, my swim team buddy in the '60s. Her contagious team spirit, her gratitude for family and friends, and her hysterical ways of bucking cancer will pluck at your heartstrings as you read…and inspire you to face adversity with a belly laugh."

— Jenifer Webb, MOT, retired occupational therapist and hospice worker

"Now compiled as the book *Ride, Baby, Ride!* Leilani's Monday e-mail updates have brought much humor and inspiration into our home. The weekly reports of her long journey through chemo, cat scans, pet scans, doctor visits, and the like have led my wife Norma and me down many lanes of laughter and (a few) tears. The shining spectacle of Leilani's sense of humor, strength, and courage has uplifted both of us as we travel life's uncharted byways; we are grateful!"

— Richard D. Lower, Retired Assistant Trial Attorney,
Exxon Company USA

"Everything you read about me in this book may be true, but if it is, it's only because I felt responsible for giving my wife something to write about."

— Bill Hurles, Leilani's husband

"Every one of us has been touched by cancer and feels the pain of it to some degree. But this book isn't just about surviving the trauma of chronic illness. It's about rejoicing in life with grace and a sense of humor! It's a book you could read every year to help you hold onto the ride of life with a smile on your face!"

— Terri Peterson, teacher, mom, and friend

"As someone who has had her own battle with ovarian cancer, I know the pain, the fear, the sudden dramatic sense that you are mortal and your body may not survive the struggle. I also know that strong people can get through that time by drawing on their inner strength, spiritual resources, and the people they love. Leilani Hurles almost makes that effort look easy as she meets ovarian cancer head-on with courage, laughter, and a focus on life rather than pain. There is scarcely a grumble in this book as she finds humor in every situation. 'Ride, Baby, Ride!' will soon be the mantra of ovarian cancer survivors everywhere!"

— Chris Bledy, author of *Beating Ovarian Cancer: How to Overcome the Odds and Reclaim Your Life*

"My good friend Bill Hurles is very coordinated, not accident prone, and always behaves himself. A man with remarkable hearing and phenomenal memory, he is a "True Yankee Gentleman." Contrary to what you may read about him in this book, he never does anything wrong. Leilani is very blessed to have such a perfect husband! Bill, you owe me $5.00 for writing this pack of lies!

— David Harris, friend of both Bill and Leilani

"*Ride, Baby, Ride!* is a wonderful book for poking fun at some of life's more serious roadblocks. It's humorous, heartwarming, and healthy for the soul. If you have anything blocking your road or you just need a good honest laugh in this crazy world of ours, then this book is for you. Thanks, Leilani, for your incredibly funny and truly inspiring book. I'm sure it will help others see the humor in even the worst of times as it has for me."

— D. Essary, insurance agent and aspiring author

"It's been said that we see through the eye, but with the heart. Well, the way Leilani sees the world around her reflects a heart full of optimism, humor, fun, and love. Her musings put a smile on my face, bring warmth to my heart, and inspire me to see the world more brightly."

— Ron Hadley, Greater Houston President, Big Brothers Big Sister, Houston, TX

"Leilani is the most positive person I've ever had the privilege of knowing. The courage and humor she displays as she faces recurring ovarian cancer is an inspiration to us all. As a long-time friend (and honorary member of the family), I can attest that the escapades she relates are true...no one could possibly make up the things that happen in her family! Perhaps that's what helps keep her sane in this topsy-turvy world.

— Linda S. Harris (friend and twenty-year cancer survivor)

"I've read a lot of self-help and inspiring stories of people's journeys through illness. But this book is original. It's funny as hell. It's full of poop, and Leilani's crazy antics, a cast of characters you wouldn't believe if they weren't Leilani's real-life husband, father, and neighboring wildlife. I roared in places until I cried. If anyone can teach you not to give up, no matter what you face, it's Leilani Hurles with her catchphrase, 'Ride, Baby, Ride!'"

— Tyler R. Tichelaar, Ph.D. and author of the award-winning *Narrow Lives*

AN INSPIRING JOURNEY THROUGH LIFE'S REVOLVING DOOR

Ride, Baby, Ride!

YOUR COURAGE TO OVERCOME OVARIAN CANCER
AND OTHER LIFE ADVERSITIES

AVIVA
PUBLISHING

NEW YORK

LEILANI ESSARY HURLES

RIDE, BABY, RIDE!

Your Courage to Overcome Ovarian Cancer and Other Life Adversities

Leilani Essary Hurles

www.LeilaniHurles.com or www.RideBabyRideBook.com

ISBN # 9781935586432

Library of Congress # 2011936789

Editor: Tyler R. Tichelaar
Cartoonist: Sylvia Breece
Cover Design and Layout: Fusion Creative Works

Every attempt has been made to source all quotes properly.

Printed in the United States of America

First Edition

For additional copies visit: www.RideBabyRideBook.com

DEDICATION

This book is dedicated to the lives we have all had invaded by some type of adversity. The human spirit must keep going! To our families and friends who stand beside us for a lifetime, this book is written in gratitude to your dedication and love.

A special dedication to my mother, Leila Essary, to whom I owe it all. Your love and devotion, and your teaching of stamina and determination have made me what I am today. I carry your strength with me always. I miss you, and not a day goes by that I do not think of you.

ACKNOWLEDGMENTS

I would like to thank everyone who has touched my life in a very special way. My relatives both near and far. My childhood friends who have stuck with me. Old swimming buddies who kept me going. And even those of you who have just recently entered my life. Some of whom I haven't even met in person.

To the chemo nurses Tracy, Betsy, Cheryl, and Susie who take such good care of me.

To my wonderful doctors, Dr. Michael Bevers, Dr. Paul I. Cook, Dr. Mark Bing, and Dr. Robert E. White, who get me through day in and day out, as well as their amazing staff.

To our good friends, Linda and David Harris, who travel, drink, hang out, and put up with us all year round. Besides being my computer gurus. This journey has been an incredible ride and I could not have done it without you all.

To my minister, Dr. Dave Peterson, and his wife, Terri, I can only say that your spiritual love and devotion to me has been nothing but a miracle.

I also wish to thank everyone who read and responded to my weekly email updates that became this book. I especially thank those who gave me permission to reprint here some of their replies. I must have received hundreds of replies, but I only had space to reprint a few. Whether or not I included one of your responses, I want you all to know how touched and moved I was that you each took the time to reply, and often, you were people I did not even know. I appreciated so much all of your support, your jokes and cheering me on, and most of all your prayers. Thank you!

And a very loving thanks to my wonderful and understanding family: my husband Bill, my daughter Lani, and my son Casey and his significant other Christina, and my son Dusty and his wife Michele. Also, to my brother Delmore and his wife Libby, for all your continued support and encouragement in writing this book. You are all my world. Dad, even at ninety-seven, you are, of course, just unbelievable!

Preface

RIDE, BABY, RIDE! is a moving and poignant, yet very humorous story about the challenges of facing Ovarian Cancer. In January 2010, Leilani Essary Hurles was diagnosed with stage three metastatic ovarian cancer. Immediately after extensive surgery, she began taking chemotherapy treatments for her condition. During chemo, it's easy for a person to become despondent and withdraw into a world of despair or denial. But, like Leilani, you can choose to fight. She is battling this dreaded disease with a positive attitude, purposeful prayer, and a lot of good old-fashioned humor. Creating and sustaining an upbeat outlook on any situation is what this book is all about.

Helping you overcome this disease with a good mental attitude is the book's main benefit. The idea for a book came after Leilani began writing an email she called her "Monday Update" to friends and family, giving them an update on her recovery. But her stories and anecdotes were so funny and uplifting that the emails began spreading to various cancer and prayer groups across the country. Currently, her "update" is being read weekly by hundreds of readers throughout the United States. Surprised and pleased that so many have found comfort, joy, and hope in her words, she has decided to publish her emails in book form so even more people can enjoy and benefit from them.

Those sharing a difficult time with a loved one will also relate and benefit from what is said throughout this book's pages. Leilani prays that by reading her story, those facing any life crisis will be given courage and hope, as well as have some humor brought back into their lives as they stay determined to overcome.

Contents

INTRODUCTION

All my life, I set my goals. Get married, have kids, retire early, travel with my husband, and enjoy my life. I was moving right along too. College degree, married, had three kids, taught school and coached swimming. Even worked as a customer service manager and wine steward for a local grocery store chain and then retired.

My dad, at age ninety, was having some health issues at the time. So my husband, Bill, and I moved him to Fulshear to live with us. We built him a home on our property so he would not have to live in a rest home.

Then it happened. The one-word news that knocks you on your butt, and that word is: Cancer!

So when life takes that turn, are you going to be ready? Life is a revolving door, and believe me, it just keeps on turning.

I hope my story helps to keep you and your loved ones revolving, without spinning out of control, when you receive similar news. You have to keep going, keep riding.

Ride, Baby, Ride!

Leilani Hurles

August 29, 2011

Chapter 1

IN THE BEGINNING

Not feeling quite up to par during the holiday season of 2009, I was Christmas shopping and thinking I must just have a virus. Some type of "bug." After all, I had just had my "well woman" physical and all was normal. Not exactly! At my insistence, I had a CT scan done on January 15, 2010. There it was...a tumor as big as a fist and as flat as a pancake wedged between my bladder and my uterus—all snuggled in where no one could detect it.

Already in Ovarian Cancer Stage Three, I was swiftly taken to surgery. The doctors did a complete hysterectomy, removed thirteen lymph nodes, scraped my bladder, removed about eight inches of colon and attached an ileostomy bag (a little gadget that is connected to your intestine so you can poop while your colon heals). I also received four units of blood while in surgery and another unit before I left the hospital one week later. I was then informed that chemotherapy would begin in two weeks.

That began my unbelievable adventure with ovarian cancer. Courage and encouragement were what kept me going. I soon had tons of support from loved ones as dozens of people called and emailed me for the latest news. Overwhelmed by the attention and needing time to recover, I could not respond to all the phone calls and inquiries about how I was doing. My daughter, Lani, couldn't respond to them either, so she suggested I update everyone through regular emails. And so was born my "Weekly Update," beginning in February, 2010.

FEBRUARY 12, 2010

7:00 a.m. We're headed for the first round of chemotherapy.

7:30 a.m. Bill realizes he forgot his hearing aids. Oh boy, it's going to be a long day!

8:00 a.m. Reach clinic but Bill eyeballs a Kolache Factory. I'm too nervous to eat.

9:00 a.m. Scared to death thinking about all the material I have read on this chemotherapy stuff. Bill's eating his doughnut! The clinic is awesome…beautiful, comfortable, and accommodating every need. Great staff…I feel better already. I weigh in at 140…geez, I thought that with all the body parts they took out I would be model size. Ha! Met all my chemotherapy nurses. They buzz around you constantly, taking care of your every need. Started IV and put in pre-meds. Then began drug one: Taxol. That lasted ten minutes. I had a small reaction, but the nurses fixed that and on we went. The nurses and I sent

Bill on several errands to keep him busy and out of our hair. I have to admit he is a saint to put up with all of this, but he is a man. Enough said! We had lunch and watched TV. We will bring movies next time. I didn't realize they had DVD players. About 4 p.m., the nurses started drug number two: Carboplatin. The time worked out great because Bill got to watch his show: Glenn Beck. No reaction to this drug, and an hour and a half later we were out of there, just in time for the horrible Houston Friday afternoon traffic. Home at 7 p.m. Took nausea pills and jumped in bed. Had a great night's sleep. No nausea yet…knock on wood! We will see how the next forty-eight hours go, but I feel good.

So thank you from the bottom of my heart for all the prayers and please keep them coming. Let's nip this in the booty together.

P.S. I figured out that Bill left his hearing aids at home on purpose so he did not have to hear me tell him how to drive all the way there and back. I'll be sure to drop them in my purse next time! Oh, Lani babysat Granddad all day…no disasters in Fulshear. Hugs!

February 23, 2010

One week after chemo and two weeks until treatment two. Feeling pretty good today. Lost a little more weight and have "lost my ass." The entire family has looked for it, but it is nowhere in sight. The butt bandit must have been here without my knowledge. Walking more each day and trying to sneak in a little weightlifting. Of course, the doctors limit on lifting anything over five pounds puts a damper on things. Lani (my daughter) took me on my first big outing yesterday. Where else...Wal-Mart! Okay, there is a technique to driving a handicapped cart. My only chance was to follow close to Lani and her basket and try not to take out every display and Lani's heels. And people really need to put their kids on leashes! I should have parked in the wine department and refueled. So next time you see those old people trying to get around a store on one of those things... GET OUT OF THEIR WAY!

Bill and dad are fine. I was amazed to find out that Bill actually knows how to do laundry and has not broken a dish...yet. I've been keeping count.

I have enjoyed the cards, visits, flowers, and phone calls. I am so blessed to have an incredible family, wonderful friends, and a very caring and busy prayer group. So on to another week and I'll be in touch.

I love you all.

Following this update, the idea of my saving the emails to write a book became a recurring theme among my readers, beginning with this email from my brother Delmore. He and my minister, Dave Peterson and his wife Terri would become avid proponents of my writing this book.

February 23, 2010

Thanks for the update, sis. You need to save all your emails and put them in a book. This is so typically you...funny. You have that Erma Bombeck thing about your writing. Take care.

Love always, D

March 1, 2010

Basically the same as last week. Feeling quite good and spunkier. I am scheduled for blood work Thursday and second chemo on Friday. Hopefully, I will have the same results as the first chemo and have no nausea.

Last week, I had a wild streak, and instead of my normal walks around the property, I attempted a major field trip. My two choices were to visit all our friends at the Houston Rodeo BBQ cook-off or just a trip to the mall to buy a pair of Skechers Shape-ups that I've been eyeing to rehabilitate my "gone mushy" legs. The whole point of going to the BBQ was Bill pushing me around the grounds in a wheelchair, which has me sitting eye level to all the cowboy derrieres in their Wrangler jeans. And girls, the scenery is endless. But with the drive time along with the time at the BBQ, we decided it might be a little too much. So to the mall we went. I walked the whole time and felt really great. Found my shoes...BUT ladies, there is a reason why you don't take a husband to the mall. Here are just a few of the "Kill Bill" moments. He wanders off to get free samples when I am talking to him. He got lost looking for the bathroom. He left me standing against the wall while he went to the bathroom and gave me the truck keys to hold and then thought he lost them. I'm sure the mall cops have found him by now...duct-taped to the wall next to the urinal.

Losing hair now. First to go was the private area. Don't laugh...I heard it's the rage to be "bare there." Head hair is going gradually. One of my best friends told me that my head will soon look like my thumb. And what are friends for?

Let me hear from you....I love the company.

Hugs to all.

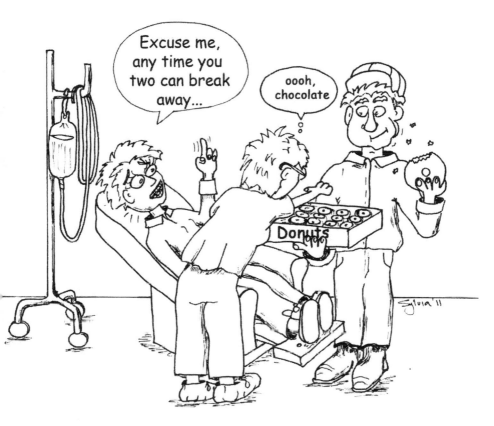

Chapter 2

Believe

March 8, 2010

Had a nice visit with Dr. Bevers, my handsome oncologist, on Thursday and had blood work done. All was okay for the second chemotherapy.

I'm almost entirely bald now. But thanks to Velma, my faithful friend and wig picker-outer extraordinaire, I now sport an awesome wig. It doesn't look like a wig at all. I'm so excited and love wearing it. Velma chose a brownish color with highlights. Not real short but full and wispy. She also liked a strawberry blond one that I may go back and get. I got a whistle from Dr. Bevers who told Bill I look ten years younger and that he'd better keep an eye on this woman! Bill informed him that he has had to do that for years...hmmm.

While we were at the med center, we drove to Memorial Hermann Hospital to visit the gang who took such good care of me the six days I was in the Signature Suites. We all cried. It was so much fun to see them again. After five weeks, losing twenty-five pounds, and getting a new wig, I'm surprised that they recognized me...but they said, "How could we forget?" I wonder what that means! I really did behave myself while I was there. There was not much trouble I could get into...with missing body parts, fifty staples, an ileostomy bag (very attractive addition I might add), and no chandelier to hang from, how is a girl supposed to get rowdy?

Chemotherapy day came and went without a hitch. Thanks for all the prayers to eliminate the nausea....They worked again. I sent Bill on several errands to keep him busy. He got us lunch at Antone's and also brought back sandwiches for the nurses. They have been so good to us. I also brought a "to do" bag for Bill to keep him busy for six hours. Snacks, movies, *Sports Illustrated* swimsuit edition that comes with 3-D glasses (Don't know why men would need the glasses; I believe things are enhanced enough), and a newspaper...it's like keeping a kid busy!

My oldest son, Casey, came in this weekend and shaved off what hair was left on my head. He's the family barber, so while he was at it, he got the honor of shaving Moochie, our Aussie mix. Makes you just feel like one of the dogs! And my friend Pam decided, when Lani told her that my bald head was more round than thumb-like, that while I slept, Lani should draw three circles on my head so I look like a bowling ball. I guess it's better than "Thumbelina" (that would be from friend Bob).

So I'm getting started on a new week. Having a few fatigue spells but otherwise fine. Lani and I are planning a mall trip. Notice, I said Lani…Bill has been sidelined from mall excursions. He actually asked me why…OMG![1]

Love and Hugs to you all. Ya'll keep me going!

MARCH 15, 2010

Feeling extra-energized this morning and looking forward to a great week. To start things off, I've been a little rough on Bill in past emails…awww! So this week, I'll start on Dad.

For those of you who do not know, my ninety-five year old dad lives with us. He has his own house on our property, close enough to monitor him but not actually have him live with us. I had all of the "dad duties" before the cancer bombshell—and now it is distributed between Bill, Lani, and (on occasion) my brother. I AM ENJOYING THIS IMMENSELY! The family is really starting to appreciate me. Just putting Dad to bed causes the bar to open! He has Bill adjust the thermostat in his house a million times a day. It's never right. Lani was the victim of trying to explain what color the chicken…the one he was eating…started out as. And I do mean the actual feather color! Then we took him on an excursion to Fuddruckers. We sat by the bathrooms (a convenience to most men) and proceeded to have lunch. Well, everyone is having a good ole time having a few beers and a burger (except Dad and me). Me because I

---

1 Abbreviation for "Oh My God!"

can't drink yet, and Dad 'cause he can't drink on his meds. I am planning the biggest revenge fest when this is all over.

Anyway, the fun should last about six more months or until my surgery to reattach my colon to the rest of the loose ends. Then I'll be back on duty.

Lani and I had a great mall trip. I bought another wig. Shorter this time and strawberry blond with highlights. I love it. Bill never knows what woman he'll have on any given day. He gets the bald lady at night.

Ladies, if you ever want to feel good about yourself...go people-watch at the mall or Wal-Mart. I thought people would be staring at me...down to 130 pounds, wig, poop bag, tone up Skechers...but no, I was a fashion model by comparison. We laughed so hard. We just sat there with our iced teas and pumped up my self-esteem. Where do some of these people come from? It's really scary. I looked better in my hospital gown!

My brother came over to have lunch with us one day. It turned into a photo-fest. For those of you who don't know my brother, or have not seen him in his "over fifty" years...he is bald. We took all kinds of bald pictures together. It's sad when your brother looks better bald than you do...it must have something to do with the ears. Now the kids say I've gone from bowling ball to the "little ole bald guy" that used to be on the old Astroworld commercials.

I have a follow-up visit to my ob-gyn doctor tomorrow. And we are planning to go to the rodeo to see Brooks and Dunn with the kids on Saturday. So next week's update should be full of stories. Next chemo is March 26th with blood work on the 25th.

Hope everyone has a wonderful week, and keep the prayers coming. Y'all really do not realize how much you mean to me. Special thanks to Sandy and Marvin for the visit and delicious goodies and to Benny for the book (which I have finished). And for the uplifting phone calls that many have made.

Hugs to all.

The following email response again sparked for me the idea that these emails could result in a book:

MONDAY, MARCH 15, 2010

Leilani, you have to write a book. I so look forward to your updates. You are hilarious. I bet you do look like a babe…130 lbs. I haven't weighed that since I was fourteen. I'm pretty impressed. Trying to picture you in your new wig! I hope your family appreciates what an incredible person you are. Your attitude is remarkable. You are one of my very very favorite people! I really want to be just like you. Hang in there and know you continue and will always be in our prayers!

Terri Peterson (wife of David Peterson, my minister)

MARCH 22, 2010

Spring is in the air. And most of you have spring break behind you. Always a good thing to get the "little hoodlums" back in school.

Our bluebonnets are getting ready to bloom so if anyone wants to see a beautiful sight, drive by in a couple of weeks…two and a half acres of them. But Bill is miserable! He wants to mow so badly. I just give him "THE LOOK" and he walks away grumbling. I told him if I wake up and my bluebonnets have been touched…his ashes and those of his lawn tractor will be amongst them!

I've been sitting out on the front veranda reading on the pretty days. I see the horses and dogs sunbathing after a long winter. Our mockingbird family has made its nest. Momma bird sits on the rail next to me and sings. She is usually quite pleasant… except last Wednesday. She was fussing and carrying on about something. I told her not to take it out on me…that I have one just like him inside (I wonder if hers wears hearing aids?)! I don't know what Daddy Mockingbird did, but he is probably duct-taped to a wind chime somewhere. (I gave her the duct tape idea.)

The pool is sure looking inviting. I'm starting to get swim fever. OMG, I'll have to warn people before I get into a swimsuit. Maybe I can invent a suit that sports an ileostomy bag. I could special order bags in every color to go with my attire of the day.

They would probably come arrest me. Man, I definitely have too much time on my hands!

I went to the doctor last week for an ob-gyn checkup. Dr. Cook advised me that Bill and I are now able to have sexual relations....Bill did not need his hearing aids for that announcement. What is it about those words that men can actually lip read? But how sexy can one be...naked...with a bald head and an ileostomy bag? Ought to be a riot!

Special thanks to my wonderful sister-in-law Libby who spent ten hours with Dad while we went to the rodeo Saturday. It was great to be with all the kids and enjoy a great day. Poor Libby made it through all of Dad's pithy comments. We left the liquor cabinet open for her! Brooks and Dunn were fabulous. The only problem we ran into was the 30 mph winds. Bill was holding onto his cowboy hat and Lani and I were holding onto my wig! Literally! People were laughing...they probably thought, "Why are they holding her hair down?" We tried to explain as we walked....We made a lot of friends. Next invention will be hair glue!

Brooks and Dunn sang one of my favorite songs called "Cowgirls Don't Cry." At this time of my journey, I feel like God is telling me the same thing.

Blood work is scheduled for Wednesday and chemo number three on Friday. Yea...I'll be halfway through! So everyone have a wonderful week and enjoy springtime. Keep the thoughts and prayers coming and know that all of you are in my prayers too. What great friends you are!

RIDE, BABY, RIDE![2] Works for me, Lord!

I received the following response to this email, surprised that yet another person thought I should write a book:

TUESDAY, MARCH 23, 2010

Gawd, Leilani, these recovery updates are so hilarious, you should publish them! I laughed so hard at imagining Daddy Mockingbird, hearing aids in place, duct-taped to a wind chime. And always, always remember that it's our spirits and experience that make us sexy as we age, not our bodies, and this goes for the men too!

Try sticky Velcro on your head and inside the wig, but hopefully as April approaches, the wind will depart, and no drastic measures will need to be taken. As the warm weather creeps in, I think there should be wigs with air conditioning!

Great words from Brooks and Dunn; heck, they probably wrote the song for you. And God just made sure you hear them.

Love and hugs from the little 'ol town of Bastrop!

Jenifer Webb (one of my old swimming buddies growing up)

---

2 "Ride, Baby, Ride" is a line from the Brooks and Dunn song "Cowgirls Don't Cry" which I adopted as my motto.

MARCH 29, 2010

I hate to admit that I'm a little down this Monday. My chemotherapy for last Friday was canceled. After blood work on Thursday, it was determined that my platelet count was too low to have the chemo treatment. So it has been postponed until blood work results this coming Thursday. Needless to say, I was upset to have been put on hold for a week. I am so looking forward to getting it all behind me. The doctor seems to think that the rodeo visit with all the wind, rain, and chill did me in. So I've been resting and staying out of trouble since last Thursday, and it is driving me berserk! But like the ole saying goes: I'll put on my big girl panties and cope with it.

A couple of other updates for you. Daddy Mockingbird is alive and well. He and momma have been quite busy, mostly because they have their nosy little beaks in everyone else's business. They have to check out everyone and everything. Poor Starr (our Black Lab) gets bombarded every time she passes the nest. Moochie (the Aussie) decided he only needed to be reminded once. He always takes an alternate route.

And I'm sure everyone is interested to know how the results of the first romantic encounter in eight weeks went. All I can say is that the "Big Bang" theory does exist!

The bluebonnets are really starting to bloom. Unfortunately, the grass is growing fast too. But the beauty is still amazing. Bill is still chomping at the bit to mow some grass in order to see more bluebonnets...but he knows the consequences. It might be the last "Big Bang" he experiences! Like I always say, "If it holds a remote, has balls, and drives a lawn tractor…it's going to be a pain in the ASS!"

One of my favorite actresses was Rosalind Russell. In her role as Auntie Mame, she said, "Life is a banquet and most poor suckers are starving to death." Believe me—Leilani is not going to starve. So I need those prayers to keep coming. All of you have been my backbone. Keep up the positive vibes and pray for platelets. Lots and lots of platelets. And to my handsome, sexy friend Keith…Bald is Beautiful, Baby!

RIDE, BABY, RIDE!

Chapter 3

TESTING THE WATERS

APRIL 5, 2010

I'm running a little behind this morning due to an appointment at the infusion center to receive an injection to increase the production of my white blood cells. It's always something. The Thursday blood work detected a low white cell count. Last week it was a low red cell count. Oh well, chemotherapy was Friday and all went well. The wonderful staff was rewarded with doughnuts. Sent Bill to Antone's for lunch again. Poor baby has no clue why I send him on so many errands. I even got in a forty-five minute snooze while he was gone. And, yes, he forgot his hearing aids again...BUT I DIDN'T!

The mockingbirds have outdone themselves on their nest, which is two-stories. It consists of one bedroom, one loft, and a spa. (That's because it was conveniently built near the dogs' water tub.) I believe I even see a piece of duct tape in there! (Good girl...I told her to keep some handy.) Now, if I have to go out there one night and ask them to turn down the stereo! And YOU know Bill won't hear it.

Dusty (my youngest) turned twenty-six on Easter Sunday. He and his gorgeous bride, Michele, just bought their first home and had their first family gathering for Easter. I could not attend because the doctor sidelined me from crowds, but I was there in spirit! I am so proud of them.

I thought the day would never come...Leilani is drinking Ensure! OMG! (Like my favorite ole woman, Maxine, says, "Don't make me use my upper case letters!") I have found a secret though—put in frozen yogurt and make it a thick shake. It's not bad. Next thing you know, I'll be taking Dad's Milk of Magnesia and parking my walker (tennis balls and all) wherever I go.

Growing up, I had an incredible swim coach during my time at the Dad's Club. He was the U.S. Olympic swim coach for I believe four or five Olympic Games. Some of you know of whom I speak...Richard Quick. He passed away last year due to an inoperable brain tumor. But I am so encouraged by his words: "Believe in yourself. Believe in your team. Believe in belief! Believing in yourself is a must. If you don't, who will?" Believing in your team is a must because your team has your back. Family, friends, and in my case, my medical team are there; let them carry some of the load. And believing in the Man Upstairs gets you through it all. So to my team: Keep up the good work. On the days I am so tired or have a few aches and pains, I know you're there. You are such an impressive bunch!

RIDE, BABY, RIDE!

APRIL 12, 2010

No reaction to the injection last Monday for getting the white cells up. The nurse mentioned I might have bone pain. Great... we'll just add it to all the list of "crapola" to endure.

I did see my wonderful ob-gyn, Dr. Paul Cook, on Thursday. (Girls, he is such a "cutie pie"—just in case you need a good, caring, personable doctor for female needs.) I went in because I had a pain in my left side. I was in bed, propped up reading my book, and all at once I was bombarded by a "comacazi" bug. It came at me so fast. I envisioned a 500-pound cockroach sporting goggles, a scarf, and combat boots! I jumped three feet and swung at it with my book, pulling my left side. It hurt so badly that I thought I had ripped stitches inside. Paul said I was fine and that I'd better be careful next time I go into battle. Of course, Bill was in the shower while I was being invaded by the enemy. It turned out to be a June bug not using its GPS system. Had I known that, I would have just caught him in midair and put him outside.

The weather is getting nice and warm in Fulshear, so I have to protect my baldness. My straw cowboy hat seems to do the trick. It still allows air to flow through. Wearing it brings back an old memory of when my parents took my brother and me to the Houston Rodeo as kids. All dressed up in our rodeo duds and getting to meet Roy Rogers and Dale Evans. The point being...Trigger loved my hat too!

We are starting to get visits from Mr. Mole again. He has been showing up all over the property. Well, now the "little nomad" has popped up next to the bird feeder. He pops up and grabs bird seed to smuggle down in his hole. The cardinal family does not appreciate the bird seed bandit.

I had a nice surprise from a good friend of mine, Dr. Mark Bing. He called me to tell me that he had a group of people marching for ovarian cancer in my name. It was held Saturday in Katy. I was so touched. But while they were marching for me, a wonderful woman that I've met twice at the Alley Theater passed away here in Houston from endometrial cancer. Dixie Carter (known for her *Designing Women* TV show) was so down to earth and beautiful both inside and out. My prayers go out to her husband Hal Holbrook and family. We have lost a real sweetheart.

Prayers also go out to Master's golf winner Phil Mickelson's wife and mother who are battling breast cancer. It seems like cancer is just running crazy. Hopefully there will be a cure soon.

Live and enjoy each day!

APRIL 19, 2010

Last week was a great week. Seems like I always have a good one right before I go get poisoned again. I have blood work on Thursday and chemo set for Friday. I just pray the platelet count is normal.

Lani and I took off for a short jaunt to the mall to get a DVD at the FYE store. We went at 10 a.m. when it opened and did not run into too many people. It felt good to get out even for a short time. We walked by Victoria's Secret; have you ever noticed that most people you see in a lingerie store you wouldn't want to see in lingerie? If they are anything like me, everything decides to sag at the same time. I look in the mirror before a shower and say to myself, "Self, what the hell happened? Nothing's where it used to be."

I have an update on the mockingbirds. There are eggs in two different nests. So it looks like we have two families to enjoy. I can't wait for the babies to arrive. Just think a little birdie nursery made of duct tape. Awesome!

I have often been asked what I do during the day. Really, it is a great question. I guess everyone who knows me knows how active I've always been. If I ever sat down, I was either grabbing a bite to eat or getting ready for bed and reading. I'm trying to be good and keep those platelets up so I'm limited on my usual time-consumers. Like shopping and malling. And malling and shopping. So, I am back to the basics of life. Doing what God expects us to do daily. Getting back to Mother Nature! Hear, See, Taste, Smell, and Feel. Listening to our bird friends start our morning with wonderful songs. The wind traveling through the trees and at night the sound of Bill's heartbeat with my head on his chest. I see the beauty of the mare in the next field tending to her new colt. The bluebonnets so abundant. I taste the wonderful foods, like the fresh vegetables and the freshly laid eggs our neighbors supply. I smell the different fragrances of roses that grow in our beds. Sitting on the veranda, taking in the aroma of fresh mowed grass. And feeling the strong bodies and rough working hands of my sons who hug me. The feel of our horses' noses so soft and cuddly. It is all right there, but sometimes we just miss it. It's like something bad has to happen for ya just to wake up and literally smell the roses.

Humor has it that old is when "getting lucky" is finding your car in the parking lot or "going bra-less" pulls all the wrinkles out of your face. I know the feeling. I have now been told that I resemble the little old bald guy in his straw hat who drives the bus in the old movie *The Best Little Whorehouse in Texas*! I really loved that straw cowboy hat of mine too! Looks like I will be wearing one of those large sun hats like the ones my mother used to wear. I bet she is having a ball "up there" watching me trying on her sun hats that I saved. Wow, something told me I would use them one day.

I have a retraction from the last update. The spelling of "kamikaze." I'm sure the June bug didn't care, but I got the spelling out of a bartender's guide. (Can't believe I'd have a book like that in my library, would you?) Anyway, I will no longer be using that book as a future reference source. No wonder a "comacazi" gets you drunk…it's not even spelled correctly!

RIDE, BABY, RIDE!

April 26, 2010

Hope everyone is doing great. Blood work went fine. I had a wonderful visit with Dr. Bevers, who explained the procedure for getting rid of "the bag," hopefully in mid-July. Chemo was on Friday. I've decided every time I take a dose of the stuff, I become "youthfully challenged"! It's like being slid, one more time, across nature's credit card machine. It just keeps drawing from you. Had a touch of "chemo fog" on the way to blood work. I left the house fully dressed, make-up, wig, and donning my house shoes! The angel "up there" in charge of fashion probably flipped her halo.

For all you "Nancy Nurses" out there...Lani and I have found another use for vodka. You know we are always experimenting. It takes bandage adhesive off the skin really well. Not to mention when your patient gets fussy, one can always take a swig.

I have decided that I should be a forensic scientist. After seeing my poop (via ileostomy bag) up close and personal every day for the last three months, I can actually analyze my stomach content. Identifying what has left my stomach and what entered my intestine has now become very amusing. It doesn't take much to keep me busy these days. I do know that one has to chew up peanuts very well or they will put holes in your bag!

The insurance adjuster came out to give us an estimate on replacing the wood floor in our dining room and den. The dishwasher sprang a leak in one of its hoses and water had, over the past couple of months, seeped under the flooring. Which brings me to A BILL STORY. The man has outdone himself! He left the water running in the kitchen sink, with the stopper in…need I say more? At least it happened before the floor was replaced. And NO, there is not enough duct tape in the world for this one! He is now a duct tape cocoon…King Tut has nothing on this man. I did show a little sympathy…I wrapped him with the TV remote in one hand and a brew in the other.

We are now enjoying mockingbird family number three. The new "casa de Texas state bird" has been under construction right off the back patio in one of our rose bushes. It is incredible how close to us they build. They are so much fun to watch. The way they start with just one twig and create such an awesome home is definitely proof that God is the general contractor and He mocks His little carpenters. Bill tries to mow, but the mock follows him around just fussing! The dogs are wearing Swat Team gear.

God's paintbrush is at work everywhere too. This spring, God's canvas is sprayed with blues, reds, greens, and yellows. The Mexican ducks (real name: whistling ducks) have migrated back from Mexico. They are so pretty with their bright orange beaks, and of course, "*No habla ingles.*" But the geese and mallards don't seem to mind.

My cousin Dick informed me, while we were talking about my chemotherapy, that Winston Churchill once said, "If you're going through hell...just keep going." You know, "ole Winston" must have gone through chemo fog at one time. It is very much like being at war. But there is a light at the end of the tunnel!

Ya'll have a great week. And enjoy this beautiful spring.

RIDE, BABY, RIDE!

My sister-in-law Libby forwarded this last email to Syd Dudley, one of her friends in Mississippi, who wrote Libby back. Libby forwarded me the following response:

FRIDAY, APRIL 30, 2010

What a writer and bright shining light Leilani is. I know that God is touched by her attitude and her talent with making a very difficult situation humorous. She is the Erma Bombeck of the non-celebrity world, and I know would be motivating to those who are going through similar problems.

It is not often that I feel so much hope for a complete recovery, but I don't see how Leilani could have anything but this. Please tell her how much I admire and pray for her and love her for her uplifting attitude.

Heavenly Father, you know Leilani and see what a gift she has for the world you have given us. She puts everything in perspective and YOU are first in her life. Please protect her, let the doctors and medicine do their job, make her well, and return her to a life that is so appreciated already that YOU as an awesome God will find her an awesome shepherd of Your Name. Amen.

Your sister in Christ,

Syd Dudley

I responded to Libby as follows:

FRIDAY, APRIL 30, 2010

My goodness...I've got to get with D[1] and write this book. What encouraging words. I feel healed just reading them. Please tell Syd that I feel the love. Life is truly amazing!

Love,

Leilani

---

1 My brother Delmore, whom we call D or Dee. He was the first to suggest I write a book and one of my biggest supporters in the process.

Chapter 4

NOTHING HAPPENS BY COINCIDENCE

I got through the first week after chemotherapy number four. It took a little longer to get rid of the fog this time. I wasn't quite normal until Wednesday. It's like being in a cage...you know where the door is, but you just can't open it! You stare through the wire bars in amazement that it's actually you in the cage.

I was telling my friend Terri through email that bald, naked, and no butt are all images my mirror gets a kick out of every day. I am mirror challenged! It's probably getting back at me for all the times I made faces at it. I guess the mirror fairy needs some attention. Maybe a good Windex job and some flowers will make up for all the abuse I've shown it the last couple of months.

Saturday night I was up late watching TV when I noticed a black cat stalking around the pool. My first thought was "Oh no, Mother Mock and her eggs are in the rosebush." I jumped out of bed and grabbed the Red Ryder and ran out the back door. The cat was already to the saloon (which is our pool house with open sides). The cat had jumped up on one of the side rails and was eyeing the sparrow nest. The sparrow family has four babies. The cat took one look at me and took off through the horse field and over the back fence. If that cat had nine lives, he just lost two of them! No doubt I scared it to death. Just looking at me would have been enough to do the trick. I was in my navy and gray striped nightshirt, bald head, BB gun in hand, and fluffy house shoes! The poor cat probably thought, "That NRA gun-toting old lady has more hair on her shoes than her head!" As I was walking back to the house, the mock was jabbering at me…telling me to get my ugly bald butt back to bed! I pointed my finger at her and said, "You owe me one, you ole biddy!" I checked on the sparrows the next morning and all of the little Mohawk heads popped up. Momma was on the roof. So all survived. FYI…we never hurt the kitties; we just scare them away. Let them go to the barns and catch mice and leave my feathered friends alone.

I am a firm believer that things do not happen by coincidence. They happen for a reason. People are brought into one's life for a purpose. God has a plan and my job is not to challenge it, but feed from it and figure out what He is trying to tell me. It's like crop circles. No one can explain them, but they are there. And heaven knows no one can explain me! But I'm here and I'm going to find my purpose. Whether it's to drive my kids crazy or just to get over these "road bumps" of life, I want the love I have for life to be contagious—to encourage others to get through life's curve balls. You can't see dirt in the dark! So I will dust myself off and not find the faults in others but the good. If you can't see the bad things in yourself, what gives you the right to judge others? It sounds like some deep meditation is in store.

Hope everyone has an incredible week. If you need me...I'm not only looking for my lost ass (no, I still have not found it), but I'll be cleansing my soul.

RIDE, BABY, RIDE!

I received another email from Terri Peterson following this message again encouraging me to write a book. She actually would keep bringing up the subject in several other emails:

WEDNESDAY, MAY 5, 2010

Dave and I decided last night that you have REAL talent as a writer and you need to keep all these "journal entries" and have them published! I'm wondering if some of this talent came from your mother the artist? Anyway, all your friends wait for your emails like they are manna from heaven! To think you could be so clever, funny, and profound when going through the worst ordeal of your life is remarkable!

Terri Peterson (my minister's wife)

My response shows that I was still doubtful about the book idea:

WEDNESDAY, MAY 5, 2010

You guys are just prejudice because we are friends. Being up-beat gets me through many a day. Ya just try not to think about the negative stuff. Knowing that I have you and Dave around is all I need. I just wish I could see you more often. I really miss coming to church, but I'm going to be good and not wear myself out. I feel like a little kid when the doc gets on me about staying out of trouble. When have you ever known me to stay out of trouble? Dave has his hands full keeping me "Heaven-ready." But I know he has good connections and influence. ☒ Dave may just have to kick me in the behind every now and then….If he can find it!

Love to you both,

Leilani

Terri responded:

WEDNESDAY, MAY 5, 2010

Well, I can tell you we are both faithfully praying for you every day so you are very much on our minds!

Terri Peterson

MAY 10, 2010

Sorry my update is late today. It's been one of those crazy days. This Thursday is blood work and Friday is chemo number five, if the lab work comes back being good.

Last Tuesday, I pulled a muscle in my back. Right between the shoulder blades. It really didn't get bad until Friday. So being the "champ" or "chump" that I am, I decided not to call the doctor because I could make it through the weekend. And it will be better on Monday anyway. I cannot tell you how painful Friday night was. There are no words to describe the word EXCRUCIATING! I didn't know that kind of pain existed. Belly buster off the high dive...no, a total hysterectomy and partial colon removal...no, childbirth...close! So I gave in and called the doctor Saturday morning. The doctor on call said, instead of going all the way down to the med-center, to try to get our regular doctor to check me out and get an x-ray close to our house. They wanted to make sure it wasn't heart-related, a stress fracture, or a blood clot. So feeling that I was in pretty good shape for the so called "shape I'm in," I made it through the weekend on pain killers and muscle relaxers. (Quite amusing because everyone who knows me knows...I don't take pills.) The muscle relaxers did the trick. All I did was write Merlot on the pill bottle! But this morning I had a chest and back x-ray. Still waiting to hear the news. The young, good-looking tech wanted to know whether I minded taking my bra off? I just had to laugh. I told him "Honey, do you know how many people have seen me naked in the past three months?" Even the janitor at Memorial Hermann sent me a "Get Well" card, saying it was a pleasure to clean up after me in the O.R. Heck, my Brazilian looking "twat" is probably in the *Guinness Book of World Records* for the most seen "who-ha," by the most people, in one day!

I believe I said in my last update something about trying to meditate. Well, the dishwasher leaked under the flooring while I was in the hospital. So the insurance adjuster came out. Now we have sealed off the den, kitchen, and dining rooms. They have pulled up the wood flooring, stripped the kitchen cabinets and sink, and tore out our beautiful oak bar. Now they are spraying the foundation to kill the mold. They brought in fans that had to have come from the Jolly Green Giant's home. I didn't know they made fans that big or that loud. If I did go into one of those rooms, my wig would blow into the next county. So to make a long story short, meditation is on hold for a couple of weeks. Bill says I should meditate while in the bathroom. Now, every woman knows that's a joke! I think I've been asked more questions, answered more phone calls, and been found by more dogs and kids while trying to have privacy in the "throne room" than any place else on the planet. And Bill, of all intruders, is the worst culprit. Let's see...where did I put that duct tape while packing up all those rooms?

Dad turns ninety-six tomorrow.

RIDE, BABY, RIDE!

May 17, 2010

I had an appointment this morning to get an injection and a urine test so I'm running a little behind. Chemo went fine on Friday and the appointment today went fine.

Lots of catching up to do since last week. Let's see where to begin. I guess...to inform all that Lani took Dad to the emergency room at the same time Bill took me to chemo. He was passing blood and is still in Memorial Hermann Hospital Katy. They are running tests and have found a tumor in his colon among other problems. Just waiting to see what they can do to keep him comfortable and to stop the bleeding. This new situation is all added to the prostate cancer that he has had for awhile. He is taking it like a champ (most of the time), and I am blessed that Lani is staying with him at night so he won't be lonesome.

I am being a good girl and staying away from the hospital germs. (Dr. Bevers, I know that's hard for you to believe...the being good part.) And by the way, Dr. Bevers suggested that I charge admission since so many have seen so much of me. Not a bad idea...I wonder if the Fleet is in?

Meanwhile, Bill and I are trying to survive by living out of our bedroom. No...literally! "Picture this" (as Sophia in *The Golden Girls* would say). Remember I told you in the last update that the dishwasher overflowed and all the flooring and cabinets were torn out to get rid of the mold? Well, the refrigerator is in our bedroom. The kitchen pantry is split between our bedroom and our bathroom. Things are stored in every nook and cranny. The bath/Jacuzzi is filled with stuff, the closets are filled with stuff, and the bedroom is filled with stuff. Wherever there was an empty space, there is now something there. We have the coffee maker, the toaster, the little oven, boxes full of necessary food all on the bathroom counter between our sinks. You can sit on the "john" and make yourself a peanut butter sandwich. And there are not enough drugs in the world to give us for sanity. And no, I have not thrown Bill out a window...yet! Can't even find the duct tape!

The air conditioning is either full blast or off. The reason being that the thermostat is in the den, which is one of the rooms shut off to the world. If one plans to be on the toilet for a long period of time and the air is on, you become a sitting Popsicle! You start to see neighboring igloos and penguins. The toilet paper is frozen solid. You have to stick it in the microwave to defrost. And you thought toilet paper stuck to your shoe was bad?

Good news though....the baby mocks hatched, and we are grandparents again to four more. We can really watch these little ones grow because they are in the nest right outside on our patio. I wish all parents were as loving and devoted to their young. It is absolutely amazing how both Mom and Dad alternate taking food and communicate with each other. And all this without cell phones. What a concept!

I would like to thank four important people in our life right now: Dr. Bevers and Dr. Cook for putting up with me, and longtime friends Dr. White and Dr. Bing for all their help with Dad. Like I said before, "God puts people in your life for a reason." I am so blessed that these four are in mine. With all the things that have happened in our life lately...just when you think nothing else could possibly go wrong...the good Lord tests you again. But I figure if you can laugh and joke about it... you can live with it! I kinda think that's the way He wants it.

RIDE, BABY, RIDE!

MAY 24, 2010

Last week turned out to be very eventful. After receiving my injection on Monday for the white cell count and getting my Monday update out, I crashed and went to bed. Monday, Tuesday, and Wednesday are "chemo fog" days. Then by Thursday, I'm coming out of it to be somewhat of a normal person. I don't know how close to normal I've ever been, but I get close. Friday, we got Dad out of the hospital and had our wooden floors put in. Now we have the house back open and we can start on the kitchen.

Have I ever told you what melodramatic excitement chemo fog causes? Well, hold onto your hat; here we go. First of all, I have finally lost most of my eyebrows, and I have shed all of my eyelashes. So a couple of weeks ago, Lani and I, waiting for this wonderful calendar marking event, bought fake eyelashes. I did my trial run...OMG! When I looked in the mirror, I saw Minnie Mouse staring back at me. I could just hear the *Mickey Mouse Club* theme song..."Here are your ears" as

I looked behind me to see whether I had sprouted a tail. But of course, there is nothing back there to sprout from. Ronald Reagan once said, "There is a purpose to each and every life." Mine is NOT to wear fake eyelashes! I'd rather be stared at by the masses.

Secondly, I was talking to my cousin Sandra who is going through the "cancer thing" as I am. (We found out about the same time except they found hers in the lung.) Anyway, we were comparing chemo fog events. She was picking her car up from the shop and had to write a check three times before she got it right. I made her feel much better. I was in bed and heard the phone ring, but I couldn't find the phone. I traced the sound to the refrigerator (remember, it was in our bedroom). I had put the phone handset in the refrigerator! Now I've got to figure out what was supposed to go in the refrigerator. I'm sure I'll smell it sooner or later. I'll probably come across it, and it will already be in its decayed state, and I won't even recognize it.

And last but not least...I was in the powder room cleaning out my ileostomy bag when my wedding band fell off my finger and into the toilet bowl. I yelled, "Oh s**t!" And Bill says, "Thought you couldn't do that anymore. I thought the bag was for that purpose." (OH, YES HE DID!) Have you ever just stopped and pinched yourself because there is no way you heard what you just heard? So what if your wedding band is submerged in poop and your husband misses the whole concept that it is impossible for me to defecate! Do you want to know Bill's last words before he went snorkeling? Ask him what it's like to fish a piece of jewelry out of the john (with a plastic spoon because our kitchen utensils are packed up). So with the weight loss, I'm no longer wearing rings unless they are poop resistant!

Thanks again for all the phone calls and emails. I look forward to them all. God gave us a wonderful gift...each other. That's what makes me so rich. The love I can give you and the love I receive in return. So I'm looking at one more chemotherapy on June 4th. Then one more surgery about six weeks after that. Please pray that all goes well. And Happy Birthday to my beautiful daughter-in-law, Michele, on May 25th.

RIDE, BABY, RIDE!

By this point, it became clear that a book was in order, and if I didn't do it, someone else would do it for me, as evidenced by this response I received:

MONDAY, MAY 24, 2010

You are just simply wonderful! How you can find the humor in your everyday experiences is marvelous. I am saving ALL of your Monday updates for a best-seller book one day. The title surely must be "How to do it right."

Love You,

Bob [Wright]

(An old friend—I was the flower girl in his and Ginny's wedding)

Chapter 5

KEEP A SENSE OF HUMOR

JUNE 7, 2010

My last, and I might add my worst, chemotherapy was Friday. I felt really bad Saturday and was nauseated and threw up all day yesterday. Feeling better today and glad all of that is behind me. Maybe I was just too excited about getting it all over with! My blood work was not the best on Thursday, but Dr. Bevers let me go on with my chemo anyway. I was so grateful for that. I will be leaving home in awhile to get my white cell injection. So it is time to celebrate with an "I kicked chemo's ass" party. BYOF—Bring your own fog!

The kitchen is coming along and should be through by this Friday. And just when we are getting the system down too! Whoever showers takes the pots, pans, and utensils into the shower with them. Just don't mistake the Dawn detergent for the shampoo. Although it seems to help the poor creatures being oiled to death by British Petroleum.[1]

Still not wearing fake eyelashes, but I do appreciate the eyebrow pencil. Now it doesn't look like my eyes drop out of my wig! However, don't scratch them if they itch. People look at you really strangely if you only have one eyebrow.

Not too long after I sported the "polished" look, Bill and I went to Bed Bath & Beyond to purchase silk pillowcases. Have you ever had the privilege of trying this athletic event for the cranium? No, your head miraculously does not stick anymore...it's like non-stick spray for pillows. You fall asleep so comfortably. You don't have to peel yourself off just to turn over. Instead you awake to strange places that scare the "poop" right out of your stoma![2] Izzie (that's what we named my stoma pal) actually growled at me. My nose was planted in Bill's arm pit! I thought my nose hair had grown back—long! And OMG the color, not to mention that the hairs smelled like Gillette Sports Deodorant. Then my next thought was a 200-pound spider decided that it would nest in my proboscis! Talk about a chemo fog adventure. A Hershey's chocolate almond bar brought me around about 2 a.m. One of man's better inventions, I might add.

My heroine, Blanche on *The Golden Girls*, passed away last week. I could watch those shows over and over. The entire fleet

---

1 In reference to the oil spill in the Gulf of Mexico that lasted three months and began April 20, 2010. The spill happened in an area where British Petroleum was operating.

2 A stoma is the opening in the body; an artificial one was made to accommodate my ileostomy bag.

must have flown the flags at half-mast...not to mention going a day without their boxer shorts in her honor. She will be missed.

Thanks to my sister-in-law, Libby, for her visit on Friday and to our wonderful neighbors Sandy and Marvin for the pre-blood work steak dinner. We really enjoyed our visit. And a special love hug out to my cousin Sandra who has started her radiation treatments.

RIDE, BABY, RIDE!

June 14, 2010

Had an unbelievably good week. After my fiasco last Friday, Saturday, and Sunday following chemo, the worm has turned. I can't wait to tell you my news. I had my first solo flight (driving by myself) yesterday. I don't know how excited the rest of the driving community was about it, but I had a blast. I hit the grocery store in full stride. And no, not with the car! I felt like a kid getting her driver's license. Ahh, nobody in the car with me. What kind of trouble can I get into? And no, I didn't mess with the cops! I should have though. It would have been fun. "I'm sorry, officer; I just had a total hysterectomy, part of my colon removed, had my sixth chemo, and by the way, would you like to see my poop bag? Bet I wouldn't have gotten a ticket!

Everybody was laughing at me last Wednesday. (Of course, that's nothing new. I'll probably have some kind of mental complex when this is over. I'll have to get Dr. Bevers and Cook to find me a handsome "shrink" I can bug). I went out the door without my hair! Fully dressed, make-up, eyebrows drawn on, and no hair! Bill says I'm always misplacing things. Not misplaced...forgotten. There is a difference. Like, why is it I can't misplace Bill? He is succeeding in getting into my non-existing hair!

Dad is getting stronger. He is still confused on certain things. Lani and I have nicknamed him "Monsieur Magoo." No crap... he looks just like Mr. Magoo. And acts just like him. He is Magoo with a "tude"![3] Dad was sitting on his porch swing the other day when a storm came blowing in. He got plastered head on with rain and gale winds. We have never seen him move so fast. It was like watching a Magoo cartoon in fast forward. Of course, he did have a tail wind to help him out. During the same storm, Lani rescued a baby bird that had blown into the swimming pool. The poor momma was trying to scoop it out and couldn't. Baby and momma are now doing fine.

Since I'm emailing people all over the world...I will inform you Houston has been HOT! I was telling a friend, Lili from Washington (state), that the experts need to come up with a new word for humid. Humid doesn't cut the mustard. It should be something like "ass-dripping wet" or wetter than a hot flash surge!

I'll close with a Maxine quote. Something I've noticed lately since I have no body hair anywhere to cover them. "Wrinkles don't hurt, but looking at them does!"

RIDE, BABY, RIDE!

---

3 Slang for "attitude."

JUNE 21, 2010

I just got home from a day of tests. Had an x-ray, CT scan, and blood work done this morning to make sure all is well for surgery in about three or four weeks. I see Dr. Bevers on Thursday for results and to set up the surgery. Please pray for great results and clear sailing for the next procedure.

I had to make sure that I didn't eat or drink anything for four hours before my tests. When I got there, they drew blood; then they made me drink some awful red cough medicine stuff (contrast) that the tech said tasted like fruit punch. Fruit punch my ass...more like fruity pooh pooh! Then I had my x-ray and next proceeded to the CT scan. My tech was a cutie pie, so I was all excited when he asked me to drop my pants to my knees and remove my bra. Then I found out it was because I had a metal zipper in my capris and metal in my bra. (Maybe that's where the saying "iron tits" comes from.) Heck, I don't even need a bra anymore. I felt like wearing a sign...HONK if you've seen this before! I know everyone at Memorial Hermann has. I'm working on St. Luke's and M.D. Anderson hospitals now.

Last week was very busy. Slowly, the empty house is becoming a home again. Bill, Lani, and I have worked our tails off going through boxes and putting things back in order. But you know how MEN just seem to be in the wrong place at the wrong time when you are trying to get something done. I do know this...if Bill asks me if he can help me do something one more time, I will be inclined to hang him from the flagpole. I haven't quite decided how to display his ass just yet....but I'm thinking (which is dangerous in itself). Like Will Rogers once said, "There are two theories to arguing with a woman. Neither one works!" But he got off the hook yesterday. It was our anniversary and Dad's Day. Have to save "flagpole activities" for another day.

A few sprigs of hair are growing back on my head. Can't tell what color yet, but I look like a baby bird. No evidence of it growing back anywhere else yet so the Brazilian look is still in. Gawd...can you imagine if it grows back bright red? I'd have to look forward to a Howdy Doody crotch! When I got ready for lovemaking, I'd have to call it Howdy Doody time!

A very gracious lady friend of my mom's just passed away, and in her obituary, it said, "In lieu of flowers, help a friend, dance, and eat chocolate." What a wise lady.

So until next week…everyone have a blast and get into as much trouble as you can!

RIDE, BABY, RIDE!

JUNE 28, 2010

To catch everyone up on last Thursday's appointment with Dr. Bevers...all went well. Surgery to remove "Izzie" (my poop bag) is scheduled for Tuesday, July 27th at 7 a.m. My platelets are still a little low, but we will deal with that when the time comes. I could have had surgery sooner, July 20th, but I would have to fast from midnight the night before until surgery time about 3 p.m. TOO LONG without food! X-ray and CT scan were normal.

OMG...I wonder what it will be like to poop normally again! I hope my ass still knows how to work. I mean the booty orifice hasn't seen active duty in six months. My brother said I should take a can of WD-40 to the hospital with me to get a lube job to get ready for action. I guess when they are prepping me, I should ask the staff to spray me. Doesn't WD-40 come with a straw to get into tight asses...I mean tight places? I'll stick a sign on my hiney saying, "You've been mooned by the best!"

Do-rags were on sale at Wal-Mart this week. I bought two more for my wardrobe. When I rest, I turn the rag around so the knot is in the front so I don't get a headache with my head on the pillow. I had taken a nap with a rag on and gotten up and gone to the kitchen. Lani came in and said I looked like a "white" Aunt Jemima. Poor Aunt J. has never been so skinny. If they turned me sideways, they'd never find the syrup bottle in the refrigerator. My bottle would have my arms up over my head to keep my boobs from sagging. Of course, we are at a point now of NBN: No bra needed!

Two of my friends, Benny and Carol, took me out to dinner at one of our favorite places in Fulshear...Ray's Grill. One thing I have to fill you in on is that Benny has humongous boobs...no, I mean all natural huge bazookas! We can laugh about it now, but Benny choked and could not breathe. It's the first time (without it being a practice) that I had to use the Heimlich maneuver. It really works! After it was all over, I told Benny she nearly died. It took me forever to get beneath her knockers! See, there is a reason God is helping me recover. He has other things for me to do.

Dale Evans once said, "Cowgirl is an attitude really…a pioneer spirit, a special American brand of courage. The cowgirl faces life head-on, lives by her own lights and makes no excuses. Cowgirls take a stand; they speak up. They defend things they hold dear." It's like she knew me and what I feel inside.

RIDE, BABY, RIDE!

Chapter 6

KEEPING YOUR CHIN UP

JULY 5, 2010

Feeling great and gaining strength every day. Taking rides in
our golf cart, planting seeds, pulling a few weeds, AND EYE-
BALLING THE SWIMMING POOL! I can't wait.

Hope everyone had a delightful 4th of July. We just stayed at
home and watched ole movies like *Yankee Doodle Dandy* and
watched the fireworks go off across the back pasture. The cows
and horses were not amused at all. Our black lab, Starr, hid in
the closet...not amused either!

A hair sprouting update...only a slight fuzz so far...can't really
distinguish color yet. Bill and Lani both say it looks salt and
pepperish. Hey, we are looking at one sprig every two inches,
a baby bird's tuff, a twelve-year old boy's mustache, or a Chi-
huahua's butt hair! All guesses at this point are pre-mature.
SO—I need help from the "peanut gallery." I have started a
new project called "Leilani's Stimulus Package." Unlike "oth-

ers," hopefully mine will work. It is a program to stimulate my hair growth. All suggestions are welcome. I've got plenty of time on my hands and room on my head to try all remedies thrown out. Please submit your valued proposals by email.

Lani and I were out on one of our get-away drives when we ran into some road turbulence. We hit a crater (big enough to be named), and I bounced right into the roof of the truck. Not to fear, my "bought hair" saved me. Forget the seatbelt; my wig was the superhero. Therefore, my wig has earned a super heroine name. I now proudly wear my brain case protector, my rugged rug that is now known as "Penny Peruke." (Look up the word peruke[1]....I feel like Bill O'Reilly at the end of his show teaching us all new words. The lady at the wig shop taught it to me.)

I have started the calendar countdown. As of today, I have twenty-two days until "Izzie" is removed. I have been waiting since January 29th for this. Major celebration after this surgery! Probably deserves a group "CANNONBALL" in the pool with everyone drinking his or her drink of preference. Mine will certainly be an adult beverage!

Every day, someone is making the world a better place. Helping others by sharing life experiences to improve their spirits. Just making them feel like they are not alone. I hope we can all show the hero or heroine in ourselves. We can all make a difference.

RIDE, BABY, RIDE!

---

1 A man's wig of the seventeenth and eighteenth centuries, usually powdered and gathered at the back of the neck with a ribbon; periwig. (Dictionary.com)

The next day, I received the following email. I actually received several emails I like this one to let me know my emails were being forwarded to others and I was being prayed for, both of which I found deeply moving and reaffirming:

JULY 6, 2010

Hi Leilani,

I am Libby's "crazy" friend from MS[2] and I just wanted to drop you a note to let you know how inspiring you have become to each of us. I forward your emails to the group I work with and I know that they forward on to others who are ill or to ones that just need to be lifted up. Your strength and courage are commendable! We have devotion and prayer request in our staff meeting each Monday and want you to know we have you on our list and are praying for you by name. We know your surgery is scheduled on July 27 and will be praying that you can throw "Izzie" away. Please let us know if you have any other specific prayer request…we know this one on the 27th is a big one! Are you sure you're not Erma Bombeck's daughter. ☺

Thanks,

Brenda (Ferguson)

(A friend of my sister-in-law, Libby, whom I have never met)

July 12, 2010

Hope everyone had a great weekend. We stayed inside most of the week just to stay dry, but what a beautiful weekend. I had to do something to turn on my ignition, so I worked on cleaning out my closets. Every time we drive up to the Salvation Army center, they are like, "OMG! Here she comes again! Hide! It will take all day to unload the crap out of their truck!" It looks like roaches running from Raid or the "lawn mower pushers" running from the Border Patrol. They are saying to themselves, "That woman is mentally disturbed and needs a 'special bus' to get around."

It is that time of year again...Yellow Jacket Season! This is like war around here. They love to build their nests in our outdoor saloon. But I am armed and ready! My holsters are loaded with huge cans of wasp spray. I am an expert at shooting left- and right-handed simultaneously. (Hey, it keeps me busy.) I dress up in my yellow and black tee shirt, black shorts, (no stinger, only because there is no ass to attach one to), and my black do-rag with the "peace signs" all over it. "Incognito" if you ever saw it! They think I'm one of them. A war tactic used by the shrewdest of hunters! As of this week, five nests down! Just call me the "Wasp Whisperer."

Bill had an encounter with another dreaded enemy in the shower last night. A 400-pound tree roach was bathing with him. Have you seen the Orkin commercial with the roach wanting to get into the hot tub with the couple? And he says, "Are we dipping skinny?" (Which to me is hilarious....Great ad.) Well, I can say Bill saw the roach drop his towel and fly in!

And for those of you keeping up with my hair growth progress...here is the latest. I know y'all just love to hear these earth-shattering news flashes. Okay...first of all...I had to shave my legs! Yahoo! More sprigs of hair arriving every day. However, the Brazilian look is still in. And for those of you considering going bare "down under"...think twice. In hot, humid weather the "ole who-ha" sticks to the undies! Experiment with that during the winter months. But of course, you might need "the carpet" during the holiday season to keep warm!

I would like to thank the prayer groups that keep me going. I got an email from Brenda, who is in my sister-in-law's prayer group in Mississippi, thanking me for helping others keep their spirits up through the Monday updates. That's all wrong. You guys keep my spirits up. You give me the courage and strength to go on. Prayer is like vitamins for the soul. And I know God is with me. Believe me....I feel HIM. Every now and then, HE nudges me during my writings and says, "A-hem mm, keep it clean or use another word." I wonder how many celestial souls it takes to keep an eye on me during the day. They say don't go faster than your Guardian Angel can fly...it must be a major relay race to take care of me. I certainly keep their day busy.

RIDE, BABY, RIDE! Sixteen days and counting. Dr. Bevers says he's ready and SO AM I!

JULY 19, 2010

Just a reminder before I get started that next Monday the update will be sent in the afternoon or evening. I have my pre-op duties on Monday morning. So don't think I forgot about y'all.

Headed for the finish line now. Just like in my old swimming days...doing a turn going into the last lap and giving it all you've got! I'm looking forward to bowel movements again. I guess one does not forget how to do that sort of thing. Kinda like riding a bike or chewing gum. And the first movement better come quickly so I can get out of the hospital fast. My release depends on my disposal of waste! I told my ole swimming buddy Jenifer that I need a quick poop so I don't have to find other stuff to do to keep me busy. Like roaming the hallways at St. Luke's looking for cute doctors! Of course, I don't have to look very far since I have Dr. Bevers and Dr. Cook taking care of me. But it's always fun checking out the scenery. Different from the cowboys and their tight jeans and other interesting parts. With doctors and their white robes, one has to use her imagination. (Except Dr. Cook—he makes it easy, just scrubs). Now this project could get me into some trouble. Oh well, nothing else to do. Headline in the *St. Luke's Gazette*, "Ole woman grabs doctor's ass in corridor, then disappears before identity is made." That does have a nice ring to it!

Only thing exciting that went on last week was Dad's toilet got stopped up. And the only reason that was exciting is that I got to watch Bill try to fix it. Not to worry; I called the plumber before he got started and asked him to be on standby because

Bill had a plunger and a wrench in his hands. I told Bill he should purchase a "poop pole" so he could enjoy "poop fishing." Kinda reminds me of a few months ago when he was fishing for a wedding ring. He has now been crowned the porcelain "poop fishing" king. You know you're a "redneck" when the excitement of the day is locating and dislodging "processed logs." And the conversation between the guys was just incredible, unbelievable, so typical of men! It's like they are so proud of clogging up the throne! I believe it is time for a major girl outing and do not forget the American Express card. I feel the ultimate "damage of plastic" coming on! You know...where you swipe it so much that you just flatten the numbers on the damn thing!

Hair growth is progressing slowly. I wish the head hair would grow as fast as the leg ones. Brows and lids are coming in too. Head hair still looks like it will be salt and pepperish but hard to tell. Wearing the wig is now challenging due to the "itch factor" and the heat. I don't even wear it at home anymore. Too much fun scaring people, catching them off guard. Like when I go out to get the mail. I thought the UPS guy was going to fall out of his truck. He really shouldn't stare. Number one...it's not nice. And he's bald too! And I think I look better.

So until next week...everyone stay safe. I'm getting really anxious for the surgery. I have a feeling this week will move really slowly only because I want it to go fast. Keep the prayers flowing. I love you all.

RIDE, BABY, RIDE!

JULY 26, 2010

Sorry it is so late; probably some of you will not get this until I am out of surgery tomorrow. Got home at 6:30 p.m. Everything ran late today and traffic was horrible. Did not leave St. Luke's pre-registration for surgery until about 4:30 p.m. I'm glad there is only one more step...DITCHING IZZIE!

Dr. Bevers will have a big surprise in the morning. When he disrobes me...I will have an envelope on my belly with a special something for him. And since he gets my updates, I'll have to tell you all about it next week. He was laughing today when I told him to be prepared.

I'm looking forward to regular bowel movements. Dr. Bevers says I have to pass gas (a lot of it) or poop before I'm allowed to leave the premises. And since Texas ladies do not do such rude noises and things in front of others, we may be in for awhile. Of course, this situation may call for desperate measures. Like paying someone to come in and poop for you. Kinda like the ole college days where you had someone sit in for you in class because there was a big party that this co-ed just couldn't miss! This might be the start of a new business. Can you imagine the business cards: "Will poop for cash," "Leave the pooping to us," "Pooper for hire," or "I s**t and get"!

Well, kiddos....must shower and stuff my face before midnight. *The Golden Girls* will have to keep me awake until then. Up at 4:30 a.m. and out of here by 5. Have to be at the hospital at 6...and surgery at 7. So keep the prayers coming. Thanks Terri and Dave for the long distance prayer. It meant so much to me. Okay everyone, as *The Golden Girls* would say...group HUG! Love you all.

RIDE, BABY, RIDE!

Chapter 7

TRAIL BLAZING

AUGUST 2, 2010

Good (waking up in your own bed with no blood being drawn) morning!

I have no idea where to start this update. Wow! It was a rough week...even for me. Surgery went well and all was fine until I really came back into the real world. That's when I noticed the pain. Not just pain...but THE pain! I have never had severe gas pain, and for those of you who have...God bless you. I have over the years weathered three C-sections and other abdominal intrusions, but never have I experienced gas pains that even went up into my shoulders. The Good Lord and I had some serious discussions for several days on how to rid ourselves of gas pains. And we came up with a solution.

St. Luke's staff was wonderful! All the nurses who cared for me from the OR to discharge were so caring. But their food is crappy! Smuggle in your own food at St. Luke's. I do not even eat McDonald's, but I actually attempted an Egg McMuffin that Lani bought me. UGH! Needless to say, by Saturday I was ready for some won ton soup from my favorite Chinese place. Anything to push the gas out!

I have had emails on the joke that I pulled on Dr. Bevers in OR. (Poor Dr. Bevers; everyone seemed to be worried that I would really embarrass him.) Okay...I wrote on Izzie's bag, "So long, Izzie." But before surgery, when we were all chit-chatting, I handed him an envelope with a note. It said..."Mike, since you had the idea that I should start charging admission to see my who-ha, I am putting you in charge of ticket sales. Please charge the janitor double." There were also tickets made up which said, "Admit one to showing of Leilani's who-ha. $1.00 each." I believe he told me that he collected $20.00. So add twenty more who-ha viewers to my registry.

After several pleas for help to get rid of the pain, the Good Lord popped an idea into my head. I could not release gas while on my back. But on either side, I could manage some re-lief. However, along with the toot comes a little surprise...so... Lani stood behind me with the bedpan. Johnny Bench would have been proud. Then I stuffed pieces of Kleenex in my butt (just precautionary). As I let her rip, Lani held the bedpan and caught any debris that should not be in a regular toot. But the Kleenex cushioned the blow just in case. Have to tell everyone I nearly lost Lani after the first attempt. The aroma was so bad she had to leave the room. The nurse brought room spray and we concocted a warning device. Fart Flag Alert! If anyone saw it flying outside the door...no one entered! I hope that Febreze invents Fart Filters or maybe Fruit of the Loom can start making underwear that targets toots. The ones that get away!

Still getting settled. Hope everyone is doing well. I will try to get with everyone as soon as I can. Thanks for all the love and caring thoughts. I love you all. So until next Monday...RIDE, BABY, RIDE!

P.S. Those are natural gas clouds over Fulshear.

AUGUST 9, 2010

Not much going on. Since I have been grounded by Dr. Bevers for awhile...no driving, no swimming, no sex, no eating of nuts, etc. I am forced to pass my time by catalog shopping. Dr. Bevers has not taken away my credit card...yet. Although, I think Bill is going to discuss it with him. Bill said I didn't spend half as much at the mall! I ordered a really nifty item today. A "fanny lift brief." Since my derriere no longer exists...I can get added help with this neat little gadget. I haven't found anything to help with the sagging bosoms. Still looking! Other than that, I just watch the family bustling around me. I have energy, but I am not allowed to use it. So I'm concentrating on growing my hair back and getting "Izzie's" hole healed up.

Dad is driving everyone completely nuts. Poor Lani has the task of taking him to the dentist tomorrow. Yes, I said dentist.

Ninety-six and he still has his own teeth. He is convinced that one is loose. Go figure! I don't know what is in the contents of his "inner" battery pack, but we would love to market it. His body has no idea of its age. If one reminisces about his years, I would say we would be talking about a battery with these ingredients: a bottle of scotch, Budweiser beer, golf clubs, fishing gear, and boat (must be that Evinrude motor), an American flag, Eagle Scout stuff, and a World War II Silver Star, Purple Hearts etc. All in all, not a bad battery pack...just add a can of ornery and we are set. Lani and Bill are taking the brunt of it... soon they will resemble me...after pulling all their hair out.

Surgery checkup is on Wednesday with Dr. Bevers. Maybe I can add an activity to my "What I can do" list...something besides wipe my ass. At least I have to do that now! Football season is starting and I will be all wrapped up in my favorite sport. Got to keep my Texans and Cowboys in the win column. Although I think the Jets and the Dolphins might have a good year. Ahhh...muscular, sweaty men in tight pants....Yep, I'll be busy!

So, love to all of you and keep the prayers coming. We are not out of the woods yet. Next eighteen months are critical. Pray for no return of ANYTHING!

RIDE, BABY, RIDE!

AUGUST 16, 2010

Best news yet...saw Dr. Bevers last Wednesday and all looks good. Pooping system is working like it should. Hopefully, there will be no future problems. My posterior "blow hole" is a little narrow and Dr. Bevers said that sometime in the future I might have to have it stretched. Guess that is the true meaning of a "tight ass"! Blood work and pathology reports were good. I will go back for blood work in three months. Please continue to pray for NO CANCER RETURN. The incision looks great. I was given the okay to swim as long as I do not "overdo." I started swimming twenty laps a day, and now have worked up to forty...along with some water aerobics. It is amazing how much better I feel both physically and mentally. Being active is half my personal battle.

Last week I told you Dad had a toothache. Lani took him to the dentist last Tuesday and the doctor pulled the bad tooth. Dad was not a happy Mr. Magoo! He was the biggest baby. Actually wanted my sister-in-law Libby to spend the night with him. You would have thought it was some major medical emergency. Anyway, we convinced him he was not leaving this world Tuesday night and all was okay. The dentist said a soft diet, and I told him he gets three meals a day...frozen, micro-waved, or take out...we will make sure it is soft! With all the special diets around here...Bill's no salt, Dad's soft, Lani's no carbs, and mine whatever I can stuff in my mouth to help me gain some weight...it makes for an incredibly active kitchen!

I told you I have been doing my laps. Well, the bathing suit look has brought a whole new meaning to OMG! Forget the two-piece…having no ass and sagging boobs do not make for a good two-piece experience. The one-piece is a challenge because my derriere falls out the bottom. In other words, they do not make the elastic tight enough for drooping cheeks! I've decided to hand out 3-D glasses around the pool. It makes the body look like the *Playboy* Bunny of the Month.

Other than swimming, I am doing a little August spring cleaning. I have disposed of a lot of stuff. But heaven forbid that you throw away anything that's in the "man cave." Okay, so the ole chair and the work-shirt stay. Just not indoors near the normal things that smell good. But I refuse to keep the "air conditioned" underwear. Men's private parts DO NOT need breathing holes. I mean when they are walking away from you, the boxers don't need to reveal a picturesque view of the hiney in motion, the cheeks of the week, or whatever their pet name is for things that day. "But honey…they're comfortable." Comfortable my ass…I wouldn't even use them as a dust rag!

Have a wonderful week. And thanks to Libby for babysitting with Dad yesterday…we appreciated the break. To all my teaching friends, your fun is starting all over again…good luck! Keep the "little brats" in line and off the streets. Moving toward recovery. Keep in touch and pray for NO MORE CANCER. I guess I'll go bathe the horses. They were so jealous yesterday when we bathed the dogs.

RIDE, BABY, RIDE!

AUGUST 23, 2010

Well, as they say...I've been so busy I don't know if I found a rope or lost my horse! I'm working out every day and still trying to figure out my new plumbing system. Working out has been fun and a real challenge to try to fill out the wrinkles in my skin created by the weight loss. Our ole pal Maxine says, "To prevent sagging, eat until the wrinkles fall out." So...besides swimming and a few weights, I'll be filling out wrinkles one chocolate brownie at a time. After all, the best form of birth control after the age of fifty is nudity...and I'm living proof!

After August spring cleaning last week, Lani and I went to Wal-Mart to replace Bill's "hiney hiders." So now when I'm walking behind him, it won't look like he is mooning me through a screen door.

I had a glass of wine with my daughter and daughter-in-law last week. It was wonderful. A Washington Merlot called "14 Hands"—excellent! I'm sure no one is going to believe this part, but one glass and I was "pickled." I slept really well that night. I guess it will take practice to "up" my intake. With football season starting, I'd better get busy.

Up to forty laps a day with water aerobics. Gaining back some muscle tone now but still not gaining any weight. But I plan on making it happen to where the weight is right and the exercising is back to normal. So, I am determined that I do not want to follow a path...I want to go where there is no path and leave a trail. So...I will be trail blazing! Warning world: I am roaming the streets and the waters again, and it FEELS SO GOOD!

RIDE, BABY, RIDE!

August 30, 2010

"It's all I can stands...I can't stands no more!" (A quote from my favorite sailor...Popeye.) I WENT NUTS! Walnuts, almonds, cashews, and peanuts. Hershey Almond bars have been devoured and chocolate brownies now have tons of walnuts on them! Thank goodness my two-week probation period for "no nuts" is over. Dr. Bevers will be proud....I made it to the end. Hell, that was harder than no sex for eight weeks! Never thought I'd ever say that. Poor Bill ranks right up there with NUTS!

Combing hair now. It's actually showing through the teeth of the comb. Definitely salt and pepper color, but I can't tell if it's curly or straight. But where did all the other hair come from? I have hair where I never had it before. Even have an in-grown hair in my nose...which I'm glad is hidden...I'm sure that's not attractive. I hope Big Foot, Sasquatch, or whatever name we have for that hairy fellow, doesn't see me...he'll think I'm his mate. (I'd have to show him my doctor's orders for no sex). Egad, I could put Nair stock through the roof! Don't remember going through this with menopause the first time. It's like having a movie sequel. The original is *Menopause*, and now we have *Menopause 2* or *The Revenge of the Hidden Hormones*. The difference is having your "egg baskets" still intact the first time as opposed to not having them or the "egg highway" or the "egg nest" or the "egg escape route"...not to mention the eggs, any more!

Dad is better now that we had a return visit to the dentist. I asked Dad what they did to him and he couldn't remember. You ask him what he had for breakfast...he can't remember, but a friend of mine came to visit so I asked Dad if he remembered her, and he said, "Yes, the one with the big melons!" (That's not the word he used, but I'll keep it dignified.) Men are absolutely incredible!

I'm trying to stir up some creative trouble these days. I was told that I was a loquacious person the other day...had to look that one up. Since it was referring to me, I thought it meant sex-crazed. I found out that it is a person who likes to talk...go figure. Gosh...I was a little disappointed. I'd rather have been sex-crazed!

Summer coming to a close and September creeping up on us. Wow...flu shot time already. Everyone stay healthy, and hopefully, we can all enjoy a little cooler weather here in the Houston area. Love you all!

RIDE, BABY, RIDE!

Chapter 8

KEEP YOURSELF GOING

SEPTEMBER 6, 2010

It was a very busy week at the Hurles house. Had my teeth cleaned on Wednesday. I could just hear my mouth letting out a huge sigh of relief. I was due for a cleaning in May, but because of chemo, I was kept from being hygienically refreshed.

On Thursday, Bill and I were invited to the Texan/Tampa Bay game by one of my wonderful doctors, Paul Cook. We had so much fun. I was surrounded by an army of bathrooms so I wasn't worried about an emergency "place to lite" in case I had an immediate calling for the pooper! Even drank a couple of beers. Will wonders never cease?

This whole week we have had our back patio and deck area full of workers. We had two 3' stone wall/benches put around the patio and in the middle a 5' outdoor grill/fire-pit. It turned out awesome. The masonry work is incredible. Of course, the human scenery left a lot to be desired! And I do mean a bunch of guys with all types of: tail trenches, ass aisles, butt bayous, cheek crackers, hiney holes, and rump splits all exposed. It was a smorgasbord of Hispanic posteriors! OMG...nothing like keeping one's self entertained with bottoms...get me back to the Texan game where they have all the "cutie butts"!

I finally felt it was time to go out without my wig. I am so glad my parents instilled in me self-confidence. You can sure get some interesting stares. At the football game, security had to pat you down. The security guard took a second look at me like I was going through the wrong line. There was a ladies' line and a gents' line...kinda scary if a man looked like me. I had make-up on, a lady's Texan shirt, jewelry, and of course, I was equipped with what boobs I have left. Maybe I looked like one of those Wal-Mart cross dressers I get joke emails about! UGH!

I even got to church for the first time yesterday. I was so excited. My minister extraordinaire, Dave, and his beautiful wife, Terri, have been such support throughout this unbelievable journey. Of course, Dave keeps me amused and enlightened during his sermons, but I really felt that when he said that God puts things in us that we don't know we have until something triggers it... he was talking right at me. The strength comes from within the heart and mind. And God gives you a password to open up the heart and mind (as Dave said...something like a computer password). And yes, Dave, my password is Jesus! Can't wait for my next dose of Dave!

Have a great Labor Day and enjoy yourselves. Keep in touch and don't do anything I wouldn't. I guess that leaves everyone wide open!

SEPTEMBER 13, 2010

Had a super week...except for two things which I'll bring up later. Hey, my Houston Cougars won, the Texans won, Bill got a new hearing aid for his right ear (he lost the first one mowing...don't ask), had a Saturday meal with our good friends Linda and David, got the back patio completed, and made it to church for the second Sunday in a row! I'm sure St. Peter fell off his "angelic perch" at the Pearly Gates!

Came in from my daily swim yesterday and had a blast from the past. There was a pair of men's underwear hanging on the back of one of the bar stools in the den. My mind drifted back to the ole college days—a man in the dorm alert, or as a junior with our own apartment, living with four other girls, wondering who managed to get lucky last night. Then realized it was you. Oh, those beer drinking days on the river in San Marcos. Many a "panty raid" was concocted on the banks of the Guadalupe! Not to mention learning a bunch of life's experiences that would and could not be taught in the classroom. How did we ever graduate? Talk about multi-tasking!

Now, the two things that got my big girl panties in a wad! First, I bashed my knee getting off my bar stool! Gosh, I'm so out of practice at dismounting. I don't have this much trouble getting off my horse! Used to be a pro at this. One cheek at a time. The bar stool is definitely an ass rest...so I guess it is going to take a new technique to get to the floor without the convenience of a butt! Still haven't found that thing!

Then...I try to be nice, but sometimes you run into a very difficult person. If I listened to my conscience, I'd never have any fun...life would be so boring. I'd be so bored I'd have to go out and kick someone's ass...just because. Customer service representative...need I say more? If you are looking for a job and you don't have anything nice to say, get a job in customer service at the phone company. And you as a customer had better know several languages including broken English with an accent! I'd like to think of each day as a new hill to climb or a new stream to cross or in this case...a chance to moon the phone company representative! If I had my ass back...I'd have done it. He did get one of my favorite gestures though!

Feeling really good. I do get an occasional stomach ache. It's almost a stinging sensation. So I'll have to get with my doctors on this one. Other than that, I've got the pooping deal down to a science. I could write a whole book on the woes of retraining the colon!

RIDE, BABY, RIDE!

SEPTEMBER 20, 2010

Not a dull moment this past week in the life of a fifty-nine year old woman trying to survive the "big O.C." Life is just full of surprises. It's like when the toilet bowl overflows...the crap just keeps on coming! From excitement in the out-house, the continuing saga of Dad's dachshund, organizing our game plan for my first post-op trip, and the never-ending dilemma of dealing with our two year old...oh, I mean Dad!

My youngest son, Dusty, came out to help Bill with a bunch of chores. When done, he proceeded to take a shower in our outdoor facility. When he turned on the shower, no water came out. But he heard it running. On the other side of the wall is the outhouse, the john, the pot, the crapper, whatever your little mind would like to call it. Well...it was now the shower too! And guess who got an unexpected power wash? Hint...it starts with a B and he lives here. Plumber Butch is on his way as we chat.

Dad's dachshund, Lilly, went down in her neck. Vet says a disc problem. It is so sad to see an animal in pain. Dad is just beside himself. We are keeping her comfortable, and hopefully, it's a passing thing. These no sleep nights are getting the best of us. Pain pills at midnight and 5:30 a.m. But Bill, Lani, and I are all taking turns. If not, the vet says we have a couple of choices. Not mentioning one of them to Dad. So please stick an extra prayer in for Lilly.

We have been planning this trip to Vegas since last year. That's when I received the news about the cancer. So we cancelled until now. Of course, to go requires a major strategy to leave without Dad doing one of his Academy Award performances. Everyone in this play has his or her part in the exodus to Vegas. We have set the agenda and have explained the whole thing at least ten times. Poor Lani will get to see his performance and put up with his whining. Lani should get the AWARD! It's pretty bad when watching a soap opera makes you feel right at home. Gee-whiz!

Lani had her well-woman's physical with Dr. Cook. In the waiting room was a little girl who decided to target me as her entertainment while waiting. Out of twenty-five other people...why me? Whatever happened to leash laws? Anyway, she brought me a magazine to look at and pointed to Tony Romo. I told her he is cute, rich, and not married. (Probably not rich for long the way Dallas is playing)! She asked me if he were my boyfriend and I told her no, but that these days even Mr. Clean looks good. He lives in the cabinet, doesn't talk, has a great body, and keeps his arms folded so it is impossible for him to hold a remote.

Have a great week. I will be thinking of you all while I'm roaming the streets in Vegas.

RIDE, BABY, RIDE!

SEPTEMBER 27, 2010

All in all, a very good week. But as usual when you've been gone for five days, there are always things waiting for you when you return. Bill will probably be mowing for the next few days, which is a good thing...keeps him busy and out of my hair! Ha, I can say that now, the length is about an inch...to be exact!

Las Vegas was a blast. Of course, just having a normal poop is a blast for me. We left early Tuesday on Southwest Airlines. One of the flight attendants was a hoot. He had everyone in stitches the entire flight. We had a conversation about cancer...which started when talking about my hair. Said he'd gone through skin cancer and his sister is a five-year ovarian cancer survivor who started out with dark brown hair, but after her chemotherapy, it came back red! OMG can you picture me with that dilemma! Probably would have put me in the psycho ward for sure! My kids think I'm Psycho Mom anyway.

Once in Vegas, I let it loose. Drank beer and wine all day, shopped till I dropped, and even met Pete Rose. Pete signed some baseballs for the kids and a jersey for me. He even talked to Lani on the cell phone. It was really nice of him to spend so much time with me. Pete told Lani that her mom was "a trip" and asked me if my husband knew I was out loose, roaming the streets (should be Rome-ing the streets since we were in Caesar's Palace).

Only had to put out an Amber Alert one time for Bill. Couldn't find his ass anywhere. It's just like telling the kids to stay close and don't talk to strangers. The security guard was laughing... he commented, "Why is it always the husbands who get lost?" Go figure! Yes, finally found Bill at a blackjack table with five missed calls on his cell. You're right...he didn't hear it ring. No... we are not going there.

Yesterday, I was trying to get the laundry done when Dad decided to fall out of the rocking chair on his front porch. He is fine. I guess now I'll have to add "porch patrol" to my duties. A few new gadgets need to be invented. A "falling out of chair" parachute, along with rubber pajamas, soft concrete, seatbelts for rockers, and Depends that bounce. Dad used to be in the ROMEO club (Retired Ole Men Eating Out) with his buddies, but he has now moved to the PVP club (Pops Versus Porches).

September is Ovarian Cancer Awareness Month. Please say a prayer for a cure for all cancers. Teal is the ovarian cancer color...wear it with hope and pride! Don't whine when it hurts... do something about it. Be Aware!

RIDE, BABY, RIDE!

LIFE WITH LEILANI

Me in first grade at Will Rogers Elementary School 1957 in
Houston, Texas. Just look like trouble, don't I?

Me in fourth grade
at Memorial Drive
Elementary School
1960 in Houston,
Texas. No, I didn't
get kicked out of
the other school...
we moved!

Me, my junior year
at Memorial High
School 1968 in
Houston, Texas.
I was a Texas State
swimming
champion at this
time of my life.

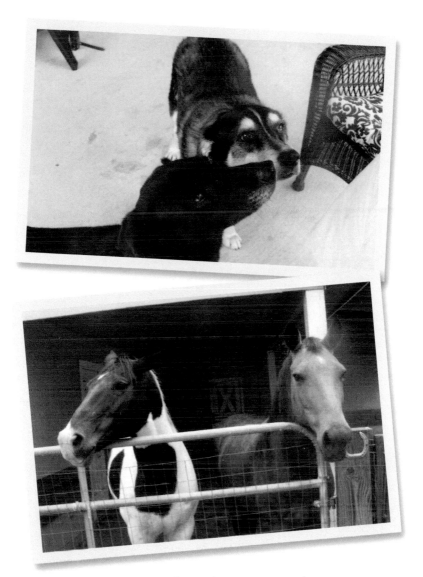

Top picture: Our babies Starr (black Lab mix) and Moochie (Aussie mix). Both spoiled rotten!

Bottom picture: The "big" babies. Bud (black and white American Paint) and Poco (Buckskin). Their barn is equipped with a bunkhouse.

Top picture: My mother, Leila Essary, to whom I dedicated the book, with my daughter, Lani and me and the Houston Firemen from the incredible Houston Fire Dept. 1993. We order their calendar every Christmas…for charity of course!

Bottom picture: Our good friends, Linda and David. Our support through it all and our running buddies.

Top picture: Summer 2011: Granddaughter Karleigh, husband Bill, grandson Braden, and daughter-in-law Jennifer.

Bottom picture: Thanksgiving 2010. My hair was starting to grow back from the first bout with cancer. Top row: Nephew Walker, brother Delmore, nephew Ryan. Middle row: Daughter-in-law Michele, daughter Lani, dad (Magoo), sis-in-law Libby. Kneeling: my son Dusty, me, son Casey.

Top picture: My handsome Dr. Bevers and me. Right after I started chemo the second time around. You can see the patch where they inserted the port.

Bottom picture: My handsome Dr. Cook and me. I am sporting wig #4 which I named Mary Lou.

Top picture: Me out in our saloon by our pool. This is our get-away to watch football games and have a wine or two!

Bottom picture: My wonderful husband Bill and me on a night out in Las Vegas six months before I was diagnosed with ovarian cancer.

Chapter 9

HITTING FULL STRIDE

OCTOBER 4, 2010

Monday again! Hope everyone had a great week. The Hurles house was a bed of activity again. The Good Lord has His way of keeping us occupied.

Lani had an appointment with Dr. Cook to get the results of her physical on Tuesday. It was so good to see him again. And Lani is doing fine. It's always a pleasure to get a hug from a good-looking doctor!

Mr. Magoo (Dad) fell off his rocking chair again. I guess you could say he is "really off his rocker"! He tries to get up using his walker and slips down to his knees. It amazes us how he stays so resilient...I guess knee pads will be part of the protective gear, to add to the rest of the stuff he uses while roaming the porch. His pajama bottoms were drooping, so I asked him, "What happened to your pants?" His ass was sagging major. I figured out it was the "generic" Depends! They were a lot

cheaper....Now I know why. Should be like Wrangler jeans....
They come in classic, low rise, and relaxed or sagging fit.

Had dinner with our friend Linda at Collina's Saturday evening
and a nice visit with my brother and his wife on Sunday. The
weather this weekend was beautiful so we sat out in the saloon
all day Sunday watching the football games. Go Texans!

My friend Pat sent me an email that ended with a quote that
sounds like something my buddy Maxine would say: "Life
should not be a journey to the grave with the intention of arriving safely in an attractive and well-preserved body, but rather to
skid in sideways, chocolate in one hand, wine in the other, totally worn out and screaming 'Yee Haw, what a ride!'" Sounds
just like me right down to the RIDE. And what a ride it has
been and I'm still thinking of places to gallop off to and cause
a little trouble. All right, lots of poop stirring!

Have a wonderful week and enjoy this beautiful weather.

RIDE, BABY, RIDE!

OCTOBER 11, 2010

Instead of writing about my life...I'm starting to get one. I'm
returning to my ole feisty self and feeling like I'm getting more
energy each day. The water has been too cool the last few days
to do my laps so Lani and I have been riding our bikes two
miles a day. Still lifting weights and starting to look like I have
normal skin instead of the droops. Well, you know, what is

normal for sixty-year old skin tone. When you hit sixtyish, you'll know what I mean.

But getting back to the grind means back to cleaning the house and feeling like the "hired help" again. I've decided that cleaning ought to be a four letter word. Right up there with the "big-uns"! It's like a day job without the paycheck. I have scrubbed, purified, disinfected, tidied up, swabbed the decks, polished, swept, sponged, flushed, and dusted. I am pooped out! (I guess I should use another word for tired considering my problem.) I may have to invest in bidets! Do bidets clean themselves? I'll invent one with a motor driven brush, and when the water goes everywhere, I'll throw in the Lysol. It would probably clean all around that sucker! Add laundry detergent and you could wash your clothes. I'll patent the "Make My Day Bidet."

Bought some new clothes to go with the feisty "tude." Some things, though, are not meant for those of us of the "hot flash" age. I tried on a pair of capris that were so low-waisted my "who-ha" could smile at the public! Or the public could smile at the pubic! It's like they should have warning labels on those things.

Hope everyone is sitting! I got a haircut! My friend and hair dresser Velma fixed me up so I didn't look so scruffy! Going to keep it really short. It's just way too easy to take care of.

Have an appointment today with Dr. Bevers. First checkup since surgery. I'm sure blood work and the works are in order.

Please keep sending the thoughts for NO MORE CANCER! I'm a little nervous.

September was Ovarian Cancer Month and October is Breast Cancer Month so please don't forget the "Ta Ta's" in your prayers. Remember, prayer is the world's greatest wireless connection. And it doesn't cost a thing.

RIDE, BABY, RIDE!

OCTOBER 18, 2010

Bet you thought I forgot! No...just out roaming the streets. Get to start this update with great news. My blood work came back and my CA-125 was "0." Negative! So now we start on a new three months. Next blood work will be in January. At least I can relax through the holidays, and then I'll be nervous again after New Year's.

It has been a very busy week. It's like I can rise and shine, but just not at the same time. Ever feel like you've had too much coffee in the morning? Me neither!

Lani and I got a chance to see the play *Peter Pan* at the Alley Theater last Wednesday night. It was wonderful! I had forgotten how much I had enjoyed that story growing up. I guess we all keep that little bit of Peter in us. There are times we just don't want to grow up!

Friday and Saturday, Bill and I were busy with my swim team reunion. The Dad's Club Reunion was a huge success. Old friends, coaches, and rivals showed up (over 200 people) to revisit the "good ole days." As they say, "Yesterday is history; tomorrow's a mystery." Next reunion, we will know what the mysteries were.

Tomorrow I have a doctor's appointment. Dr. Bevers set me up with a "BUTT STRETCHER"! My doctor is afraid that the section of my colon that he connected to my rectum is too narrow. So this new guy is supposed to analyze the situation and decide whether he needs to do something with the ole "blow hole." So please refrain from any "bottom" jokes. I've already had an earful. Or should I say a butt-load of hiney humor?

So tonight, I will close with one of my favorite quotes from *Peter Pan*. Peter says, "I'll teach you to jump on the wind's back—and if there are more winds than one, they toss you about in the sky—they fling you for miles and miles—but you always fall soft into another wind—and sometimes you go crashing through the tops of trees, scaring the owls, and if you meet a boy's kite in the air you shove your foot through it. The stars are giving a party tonight. Oh Wendy, when you are sleeping in your silly bed you might be flying about with me, saying funny things to the stars." I wish all of you a journey in life that has you bouncing off the stars and catching your dreams.

RIDE, BABY, RIDE!

OCTOBER 25, 2010

What does one wear to a "butt stretching"? Yes, on November 3rd, yours truly will be going through a colonoscopy equipped with balloons. So I am deciding on what fashion statement to make. I guess a thong is out! Let's see; so far in 2010, I've had two major surgeries, five blood transfusions, six chemotherapies, two CT scans, and numerous blood works. Now I add a colonoscopy and a mammogram to the mix. Not to mention the ole "who-ha" is in the "Privates Hall of Fame"! Speaking of the infamous area...the Brazilian look was in and now out. The scratch-the-snatch was in and now out. I no longer need the anti-itch products and do not have the embarrassing itch moments. Now, where is the Nair?

I dragged Bill to Coldwater Creek to do a little shopping and told the ladies to keep him company while I looked for something exciting that was on sale. He sits on the comfy couch with his coffee, reads his paper and talks to the girls while I shop. He knows I carry the duct tape in my purse so he doesn't dare try to escape! Perfect set-up. I always ask his opinion and then choose the opposite of what he likes—works every time. Shopping helps me stay young at heart; of course, the rest of the body needs help...at least the body parts that are left.

We had dinner Saturday night with our good friends Linda and David at Collina's. Have you ever gone into a room and forgotten what you went in there for? I mean you just thought of something you needed and within thirty seconds you forgot what it was. Well, I did just that; I was on a mission to get a bottle of wine for our Italian dinner at Collina's. Now, can you believe that Leilani would forget a bottle of wine? I'm telling you the Earth is near its end! It is so funny what age does to the mind. And now I don't have chemo brain to blame. I guess from now on I'll have to hurry to get where I'm going so I don't forget my destination. I wonder if a cop would fall for that: I'm speeding because I have to hurry to get to where I'm going so I don't forget. Geez!

I lost a really good friend yesterday. My friend Pamela from my Kroger days had to have a foot amputated due to diabetes. Her heart just couldn't take it. But knowing my Pam, she has Heaven roaring with laughter. And I will always remember our good times together. God bless her.

I'm getting my haircut tomorrow. My pal Velma is going to check it out to see what can be done. Gosh...I hope I don't forget where I'm going! I'll drag Bill along so I can get a free lunch out of the deal! See, he is good for something. Anything but fashion decisions.

Have a great week everyone. Don't let the goblins get you! I haven't decided what to be this year. I could dress up in doctor's scrubs and be a "butt stretcher"!

RIDE, BABY, RIDE!

Chapter 10

SAIL, BABY, SAIL!

NOVEMBER 1, 2010

Hope everyone had a Happy Boo Day! Every year, Fulshear Farms has a Halloween hayride for the little goblins. They start out at home base and have dinner and games before "hitting the hay" and scaring all of us olc guys. When they made their yearly visit Saturday night, there must have been thirty of the little brats. It was so much fun. Bill and I dressed up as the "Boo Brothers"! I was the ghost who had lost its ass and Bill was the one with hearing aids! I guess Wednesday I'll be the ghost getting my boo-tie stretched!

Getting ready to vote tomorrow and start taking that nasty stuff you have to drink before a colonoscopy. Politics and colonoscopies kinda go hand-in-hand, don't they?

I was honored to attend a get-together for the Big Brothers Big Sisters at Minute Maid Park. I was invited to sit in for my dad (he founded the Houston area BBBS) at a photo shoot for its sixtieth anniversary. Thanks to all the "Bigs" who take a little brother or sister under their wings to give a little extra love and attention in their lives. It was truly heartwarming to hear the many stories of the kids whose lives have been inspired by their Big Brothers or Big Sisters.

My new friend, Michelle from Mississippi, whom I have never met but feel attached to at the hip...or some body part that I have left, mailed me a gift. She is a soul-mail friend like others whom I have met through this unbelievable cancer journey. Between Libby (my sister-in-law), Michelle, and the prayer group, I have been introduced to *The Sweet Potato Queens*. If you are not familiar with these ladies, go grab a Sweet Potato book. They are written by Jill Conner Browne. You will be totally encased in her humor. I was sent a book (signed by the author), a tiara, a wig, a sweet potato tee shirt and the coolest sunglasses on the planet. I can't wait for the sun to wake up tomorrow morning so I can grace Fulshear, Texas with my new attire! The town worries about me anyway; they'll probably commit me now. I'll walk around with one of Jill Conner Browne's "Fat Momma's Knock You Naked Margaritas!"

Well...time for sitting out on the front porch...sipping a wine and enjoying the lizards jumping, the frogs hiding until dark, hawks stalking, and all the other relaxing scenery life has to offer. I am so blessed that Fulshear offers such beauty! Tomorrow, I will be on the all-clear liquid diet and that gross drink. Hey... white wine is a clear liquid!

Special thanks to my friend Dr. Mark Bing for coming out to check on Dad yesterday. Yes...we were having a Dad moment. Nothing bad...a sore throat. Of course, we had to pay him (Mark) off with a hot dog. We were grilling for the Cowboys game (don't go there) with a few of our friends, and Mark couldn't stay for the burgers and steaks. You are a sweetheart, Mark. Thanks!

RIDE, BABY, RIDE!

NOVEMBER 8, 2010

GREAT NEWS! The colonoscopy went without a hitch. No stretching was needed and NO CANCER was detected in that area. Dr. Hochman was just full of good news. We were laughing before the procedure because I told him I had made a map of my ass and put a big star on the entrance that said, "You are here!" Just like in the malls so you don't get lost. I believe it was a mutual thought that I didn't need to have poop the size of tree trunks. So before the anesthesiologist sent me into Margaritaville, the "posterior peeper," "the potentate of poops" asked me whether I had any other questions. Being the honest person that I am, I told him, "I have to poop!" The nurse started laughing and said they have this machine called the "poop vacuum"...that's the last thing I remember. Thank goodness...I don't think I even want to know what that thing looks like!

The worst part of any colon-related procedure is the preparation for it. OMG...it is awful. To cleanse the anal abyss you have to drink this nasty stuff along with clear liquids the entire day before. It's a good thing we have our own water well. Otherwise, the water bill would have been the national debt. We'd have to pass a stimulus package of our own for water usage. (Hey, they have one for everything else)! The "flush fairy" was kept busy. I can't begin to tell you how many times I "cranked the tank." The septic system was waving a white flag. It's like the famous line in the movie *Christmas Vacation*: "Merry Christmas...the sh**ter's full!" I'm going to buy stock in whoever makes Vaseline Petroleum Jelly. I've renamed my butt "Vaseline Valley." When the doctor asked me, "How did the prep go?" I just gave him "THE LOOK" and said, "Go ahead; make my day!"

Went to church Sunday. I felt I needed to get away...by myself. I'm so glad Bill understands when I go into my "leave me alone" mood. Thank you, Terri and Dave (my minister extraordinaire and his beautiful wife), for the hugs...and for some reason, I really needed them yesterday. My body needed the real "soul food"! God and hugs!

So back to my crazy self again. To say that I'll be behaving myself is totally ludicrous, so I guess I'll go out and point my "Vaseline Valley" at someone and give him a thrill or at least put a "hiney hug" in his day!

RIDE, BABY, RIDE!

NOVEMBER 15, 2010

Feeling really good except for a few stomach aches and a constant ringing in my ears. (No, it's not my body's defense mechanism not to hear Bill.) Can't explain either ailment, but hopefully, they will leave peacefully.

A very relaxing week at the Hurles house. The horses had their pedicures; the dogs had a nice warm shower with Mom (this is a story for another week...still recovering), too cold to get the usual outdoor cool-off bath. The horse field was fertilized for winter, and we had our first fireplace "light up" of 2010.

My dear friend Pat, Lani, and I had a wonderful Girls Night Out. The original plan was to go to dinner, have a wine toast to our "crazy" friend Pamela, who passed away a couple of weeks ago, and attend her Memorial service in Dickinson, TX. Has anyone ever tried to find a "one pew" Baptist church, in the dark, in Dickinson, TX? Well...DON'T! So it was a wine drinking night, toasting Pam every time we took a wrong turn! We love you, Pamela! If you are counting in "dog wines," I only had one!

Dad is still hanging in there. I really believe the more one complains, the longer God makes you live. The man is a TRIP! And his dog is driving everyone up the wall. It's like she can hear a pecan drop off a tree in the next county and decides the world needs to know she heard it. I know the word "dachshund" in German means "the little pain in the ass"!

It's getting about time to get back on the horses. My definition of riding is the art of keeping the horse between you and the ground. I have not cleared this with the doctor yet, but I think he knows me well enough that I'm probably going to do it anyway. Dr. Bevers would rather not hear me bitch about it. Although bitching to me is just motivational speaking. Ask Bill.

My thought for the week is something I hope will help all who encounter cancer the way I did. Live your life like there is no tomorrow. Believe in yourself. I want people who have health issues of any kind to know that you can be a role model to people who are just starting their journeys. Get out there and "look great" (hair or no hair), live a wonderful life, and keep the "TUDE." LIVE, LIVE, LIVE! Remember, God answers "knee mail"!

RIDE, BABY, RIDE!

NOVEMBER 22, 2010

Sorry, I'm a little late today. Been at St. Luke's having a CT scan. Will get results back on Wednesday. Keep your fingers crossed and pray for a negative find. I have been having some tummy problems and Dr. Bevers just wanted to be on the safe side and have a look.

Which brings up that the airport screenings, scannings, and gropings have nothing on mammograms, colonoscopies, MRI's, and CT scans. I'll tell you about invasion of privacy. I mean men have no clue, but a mammogram is a complete molestation of the ta-ta's! I would just like to be able to pick out my groper. If someone is going to peek aimlessly at the ole "who-ha" and hooters...I'd much rather a good-looking man do it.

"Honey, do you know if we have an empty tote anywhere?" Phone rings..."Mom, we're playing trivia. Do you know if Donald Duck ever wore pants?" (Really?!) Ring ring again. "Mom, how are you? Do you have anything to eat over there?" Car drives up..."Mom did I leave my fishing pole over here?" Monitor goes off...Dad wants me to check his thermostat. Hey, I thought I was the one with a medical setback. Is it possible that moms are the most popular people in the world? Not complaining because I know we are the most loved. I feel so blessed to be needed in every way: cook, trivia expert, warehouse keeper, captain of organization, and dog whisperer. Yes, even the dogs come to my side of the bed when they want something because they know they can't wake Bill up. (New invention...go-to-bed hearing aids...just what every man needs is to be nagged even during the night.)

Just a reminder. No Monday update next week. Bill is whisking me off to Belize. But I'll get something to you before we leave. Lani and my sister-in-law Libby are in charge of Dad. Lani took him to the dentist today to have one of those famous ninety-six year old teeth filled. When he goes, those damn teeth need to be studied and put in The Smithsonian...right next to the dinosaur collection! Molar of Granddad, the Essaryousrex... been filled twenty times. Enough metal in that sucker to sink a battleship!

Bill and I had a wonderful lunch Friday with our friend Dick Baile and my minister Dave Peterson to discuss raising money for an educational fund started in my dad's name with the Big Brothers Big Sisters organization. I would like to thank them both from the bottom of my heart for their support. Mr. Baile helps with the money matters and poor Dave is stuck trying to get this ole broad to Heaven. Believe me, he has his hands full. Oh yeah....all broads go to Heaven! Hope I find my ass before I go!

RIDE, BABY, RIDE!

November 27, 2010

Hope everyone had a wonderful Thanksgiving. We certainly did here at the Hurles home.

I am connecting a little early to let everyone know that I received the news on my CT scan early Thanksgiving morning. It looked negative for cancer, BUT I have gallstones! Thanks for the prayers...I'd much rather deal with gallstones than cancer. So I will be zapping rocks when I return from Belize. I'd like to thank Dr. Bevers for staying up late to get me the results. I was emailed at 3 a.m. I owe him a BIG strangle-hug. A strangle-hug is for going WAY beyond the call of duty...and it leaves no visible marks! I sure hope he was up for something else at that time of night and not just for me. Then I will leave some visible marks!

Leave for Belize tomorrow morning. I will be thinking of you all and wishing my family and friends were there with me. 2010 has been an incredible ride, and I will rejoice with every sunrise for the love that has been sent my way. Remember, if you get a collect call from a Belize jail...answer it...it wasn't my fault even though I am still looking for my clothes!

RIDE, BABY, RIDE!

Sail Baby Sail!

Chapter 11

HOLIDAYS KEEP
YOU BUSY

DECEMBER 6, 2010

We're back! And in one piece! Okay...we get on the ship and the first clue that we were going to have a blast was our captain's name. Are you ready? Otto Bang. For real...no poo-poo. Sounds like a name for a vibrator, doesn't it? We all had so much fun. Went with two other couples. Our ole friends Linda and David from Houston and Lili and Bill from Seattle. (So to keep everyone from getting confused when talking about the Bills...I'll use Bill S for Seattle Bill). I was no part of the first escapade! Bill S was arrested by customs for smuggling on two bottles of David's vodka. Well, not physically arrested, but hands slapped and booze taken away until the end of the cruise.

Now...there are seventeen bars on board...how much trouble can Leilani get into on this ship? But I kinda made two bars my home. "The Pig and Whistle" and one called "Hi Notes." Yes,

I did find myself on stage at The Pig and Whistle, and I was required to sing "Ole Time Rock and Roll." Ahh, but I made sure everyone got involved...even the waiters. So after the first night, everyone was calling me by name and gesturing "superstar," which was the code for anyone who got up and made a fool of herself.

Every day, our stateroom dude (named Celso) had something made out of towels waiting for us on the bed. One night, we came in and there was a bat hanging over the bed—very clever and added a special touch to our cruise.

Linda and I both won at bingo. But we had an embarrassing moment...Bill H fell asleep during one of the bingo games. Snored, dropped the card on the floor...the works. We were all laughing at him. But in his defense, he did close the casino down the night before.

We were awakened at 6 a.m. as we were pulling into Roatan, Honduras by a tribe of voodoo people dancing and singing. Not a good combination with an ole time Rock 'n Roll hangover. Next day was beautiful Belize where we had great food at "The Wet Lizard"! Yes, that's what I said. Then on to Cozumel. There we had a Mayan dude greeting us, and we shopped and hit the bars: Margaritaville and Señor Frog's. Yes, again I was on stage at Margaritaville, but not long; they were line dancing (which is not my favorite) and my side started hurting. (Don't worry, Dr. Bevers; it didn't hurt long.) David and Bill H had balloon parrots made for their shoulders by a pirate clown. Bill's had an extra appendage to it. Yeah...guess what? Everyone was laughing. Linda and I made balloon flower bracelets. No appendages!

At the captain's dinner, we met Captain Bang. And we all went to the Mystery Dinner one night. That was really cool. They even had an ice skating show on board that was amazing. And the mystery cast was some of the very talented ice skaters. Too cool!

More on the cruise will show up in future updates. No jail bond was needed, at least for me. I can't speak for Bill S! The sweet Ms. Lili sure has her hands full. Hope everyone has a great week, and as soon as I find out more about the good ole gallstones, I'll let you know. Missed you all. Many emails were deleted because while we were gone 171 showed up. If it was something I need to know about, please re-email them.

RIDE, BABY, RIDE!

DECEMBER 13, 2010

Hope everyone had a great weekend. I for one struggled a bit with my gallstone problem the last few days. Lots of pain, tightness, and a bloating feeling, not to mention the gas. Not a good combo especially when one is strategically located within a few feet of someone else. It's pretty bad when even the dogs get up and give you a look...and you know they are saying: "And you always blame me for those and mine aren't half as gross as gallstone ones!" But no procedures are scheduled unless it gets really bad. So let's all keep our legs crossed on this one!

Still reminiscing about the wonderful time we had on our cruise. I have always been a believer in things happening for a reason. You meet people for a reason, and there ARE angels among us. On our journey, we met many new friends. I started chatting with a very nice man sitting next to Bill at the black-jack table in the casino. He was wearing a George Strait cap, so I mentioned how much I love George and how I had missed his and Reba's concert last year due to my cancer discovery. (Missing George hurt worse than the damn surgery did!) He proceeded to give me a big hug and told me I had just run into the right guy. Are you ready? His name is Allen and he is George Strait's driver! I started crying. He gave me guitar picks that George had used with George's name on them, and he said to call him before any concert, and he would get us backstage to meet George and the Ace in the Hole Band. Yes...had to change the ole big girl panties! Nothing does it like George!

I met several women who have been down the same road as me, trying to survive cancer. They loved my short hairstyle. Many women on the ship had the same style...some by choice...others by chemo. One lady named Patty was wearing a wig which she named "Lola." She had her last chemo in August for breast cancer. She admired my courage for leaving my hair short and wanted some of that bravery to rub off on her. Boy, she had no idea what she was asking for! So I played the role of "self-confidence" that day. Self-confidence...PASS IT ON! Another breast cancer fighter named Valerie was also trying to keep the spirit. I think I got her in "the DILLIGAS"[1] mode on what others think. I threw in my favorite movie line that I dig out when my opinion is asked..."Life is a banquet and most poor suckers are starving to death!" Enjoy the second chance God gave you and LIVE! Talking with them made me so thankful that I have the doctors and nurses I have. It is so scary when you have questions and you hurt and no one is there to answer them, or you have an answering service give you a bunch of BS, and then someone you never met calls and doesn't know your name or even where you are coming from. This happened to both of these ladies, so I thank God every day for my wonderful Doctors Bevers and Cook, who have been there for me through this entire ordeal, and my family dudes, Doctors White and Bing, for putting up with the entire family and their needs. You are God's gift to me! Thank you for everything.

Bill has been busy on "honey-do's." Putting out reindeer, hanging lights on the front porch, (and his ass did not fall off the ladder once, or if it did, he's not 'fessing up), decorating the tree, and running to the store for the little things I have forgotten. So basically, I'm just driving him NUTS like every good wife! Animals are getting used to the cold breezes we have had out here. The horses are huddled in their stalls and come out only for the beautiful sunshine...to roll in the pasture and sunbathe. What a life.

1 Acronym for "Do I Look Like I Give a Shit?"

So, hope everyone has a wonderful week. Do not shop till you drop! And get out with Nature and roll in the grass and soak up the sun. I tried it with the dogs—it's awesome!

RIDE, BABY, RIDE!

DECEMBER 20, 2010

'Twas the Ho-Ho-Ho-ing before Christmas week. Quick trips delivering hugs and goodies to the incredible angels on my list whose halos shine all year long. Not real sure Santa knows what to do with this little elf. I guess he's just glad that I know when to be naughty, and of course, I'm always nice! He gave up keeping up with me years ago.

Good ole holidays....I'm actually seeing the beginning of love handles, although nothing to brag about—just saying! And I do believe that I'm forming a butt! Not ready to contend with the famous Wal-Mart "butt gallery," but enough finally to see a "cheek smile." Even the saleslady in Chico's said she thought I was starting to get my ass back...I'm really proud of myself. I hated being so thin. It's just not American. I guess when I meet my goal, I'll have my hiney do a flag waving!

Battling the HoneyBaked Ham line is always a holiday joy. At Thanksgiving, it was a nightmare, but my friend Carol and I went yesterday to pick up our Christmas hams, and we walked right in and even had spare time to go to Los Tios for a drink and nachos. I did miss meeting people in line—that is always a trip in itself. Carol and Benny also met Lani and me at Ray's

Grill last Wednesday for a Girls' Night Out toast. I treasure the times with friends and family but especially now.

I do believe the Canada Geese are really confused. And I thought the mall was exhausting! When we have a cold front move through, they head south over the house. It warms a little and they are headed back north. Next time I see them, they are going west...then east. Hope they packed spare feathers, a compass, and an energy drink. Poor Moochie and Starr are wondering why they keep hearing what sounds like a pack of dogs flying.

Bill and I went to Austin Saturday to visit our grandkids, Braden (fourteen) and Karleigh (twelve) (Billy Jr.'s two kids). We took them to lunch and to the mall for Christmas shopping. What is wrong with us? I knew there was a reason that we drank! One forgets what teens are like, and then it all starts coming back. OMG...the decisions that were made. Once they each decided on the stores they wanted to hit, then it was, "What do we want from each store?" I'm going to use a line my mom and dad used to say...and I never thought I would ever repeat it: "Do you think that money grows on trees? What part of 'recession' do you not understand? The answer is not maybe... it's NO!" Bill drove...it took me a bottle of wine to get back to Houston.

We lost a member of our family last week. My sister-in-law, Libby, had to say goodbye to her father, Cecil Swilley from Brandon, Mississippi. We will all miss him, and our thoughts and prayers go out to Libby, her brother Rodney, and her mother Ellen. Cecil gets to hear the real heavenly choir for our Lord's birthday.

Bill and I would like to wish everyone a very Merry Christmas, and we hope that the love of God finds your home. The angel atop our tree reminds me of all of the wonderful family and friends we have and how blessed our lives are. Love from the Hurles Family to yours!

RIDE, BABY, RIDE!

DECEMBER 27, 2010

Holy Leftovers, Batman! Is it just me or does everyone feel like he is going to burst?

It was a wonderful Christmas. The Hurles house only had one major issue. Santa fell in the horse field while scooping poop. Pulled a muscle in his back. Long story...but the short version is the horses got spooked and ran right for Santa for protection. Santa and poop were flying everywhere! I think next year we will get an elf to be the pooper scooper! And one to clean the shower too! Talk about a sh**ty job!

As far as gifts go, let's see... Bill received a Wii system. One of the DVDs was a sports pack. The entire gang bowled all day long. It was a blast! Of course, all of us were sore on Sunday. Santa had to share his heating pad. If bowling puts our muscles in orbit, I'd hate to see what the other sports do. I feel a new way of getting in shape in store for all.

I received an underwater Kodak camera. Takes video and regular pictures. I can't wait to use it. Just call me Jacquesette Cousteau! The Little Mermaid has nothing on me. The whole family is wondering whether Santa has lost his mind. I dare anyone to skinny dip now! Hmmm, I wonder whether it has a zoom lens? Oh what fun it is to dive!

On Wednesday, Lani took me to the gall bladder doctor, Dr. Timothy Sehorn. Lani wants to know how I keep inheriting the "cutie pie" doctors. I do have to admit this one makes the "hottie" list.

Dr. Sehorn is going to run some tests on the gall bladder to see whether it is really the culprit. He thinks it might be just an upper bowel problem. Like a small blockage. Hopefully, all is okay...I have not had any problems since last Monday night's flare up. Please continue to pray that all the news is good.

For Christmas, Bill and I purchased a chocolate cake from Buca's. If you have never been to Buca's, please make a point to go. Great Italian food and a great atmosphere. But its Double Dutch Chocolate cake should have been named "Death by Chocolate"! They sell it by the wedge. Not slice but WEDGE... it is not normal. Probably why it suits me perfectly! We served it at the family gathering Christmas Eve. It was the hit of the evening. I haven't heard so many "oohs and aahs" since...well never mind! (I send this to my minister...just imagine!)

Hope everyone has a safe New Year's Eve. Don't drink and drive—take along that designated driver. We plan on being right here unless Santa can take his muscle relaxers and heating pad with him. I'll let you know as soon as the test results come in on the gall bladder. HAPPY NEW YEAR!

RIDE, BABY, RIDE!

Chapter 12

ANOTHER YEAR—WOW!

JANUARY 3, 2011

Well...we made it to 2011!

With the New Year arriving, I have made my New Year's resolution. I am going to clean house. And by that I mean the cabinets, attic, closets, sheds, and garage. If there is any doubt, it goes! I noticed in the kitchen pantry that there are cans of veggies that will outlive me. (And hopefully, God grants me a while.) Have you noticed some of the dates on those cans? If the world ends in 2012 (according to Mayan calendar lore), then the cans will outlive the end of the world! Just saying! Millions of years from now, in the ruins, the next civilization will find a can of Green Giant green beans...still in date!

Let's see, the Twelfth Day of Christmas will be January 6th. So I guess for luck (I need all I can get) the decorations will stay up until the 7th. It's always sad taking them down. It's my most favorite time of the year. I feel closer to the spiritual world even more than usual. I've always heard that 111 or 1111 was some-how connected to the angels. I see these numbers all the time. I don't know if that's an omen or what. But I have heard of oth-ers who have this experience with certain number sequences. I wake up at night and it's 11:11 or 1:11. During the day, I look at the clock with the same results. I had to tap my spiri-tual dude, my friend and adviser, Dave—my minister—to see whether I was going nuts. I have read several articles about it on the Internet. Very interesting things written about it! Most are said to be angelic signs. My friend Pat and I were talking on the phone about it when one of her keepsake angels fell off the shelf to the floor. It didn't break. Too cool for words! It gave us both "goose bumps." Don't you just love it when God gets your attention?

Went to two parties over the weekend. For New Year's Day, we went to our neighbors' house down the road. Lots of food and camaraderie. Heidi, our hostess, always makes a dessert specialty of hers. I don't know all the ingredients, but she calls it "the orgasm"...so you can only imagine! So I decided there should be a food group named "Better than Sex" group! Listed right up there with the carbs and protein. We also got to spend time with our good friends Linda and David. Finally got to exchange Christmas gifts and enjoy good company.

No more news on the scheduling of my tests. I have not heard from the doctor's office since my visit. I have had no problems for about three weeks now, so I'm considering not having them run. Maybe just the ultrasound to look at the gall bladder. I'll see what Dr. Bevers has to say. I will pursue whatever he suggests.

Bill's back is not feeling any better either! Poor thing has been on the ice pack and then on the heating pad. Dr. Bing had an x-ray done, and at least there was nothing cracked or broken. If there were a computer key for "What the ****?" I would insert it here.

My daily life makes for outlandish stories, and I can hear my grandkids years from now saying, "Did that really happen"? And others replying, "If you knew your grandmother, you wouldn't have to ask!"

Happy New Year to all!

RIDE, BABY, RIDE!

JANUARY 10, 2011

OH BALLS! Literally...but Happy Monday anyway!

In order of occurrence:

1) Bill's back has been diagnosed as a compression fracture. Went to the specialist today and the doctor is setting up an MRI. Bill is in lots of pain and holds on tight to the heating pad and pain pills, which is totally not like him.

2) My ultrasound was done Friday for the gall bladder. Results should be back tomorrow...so I am told. Had a major flare up last week which I had not experienced for three weeks.

3) Washing machine hose leaked and water went everywhere. We have to replace the hallway wood floor...again! Twice in nine months....ugh!

4) Hank, the bull that occupies the field behind our house, came to the fence for a visit...leaned on it with his rear. I guess it's Mother Nature's way of getting us in the rodeo mode. That has to be the biggest set of "Ooh la la's" I've ever seen. (Sorry Bill.) Not counting those of the famous rodeo bull "Bodacious." Boy, talking about bragging rights!

So there can't be a crisis today...my schedule is already full. The only thing better than one wine at this point...is two! Oh well, I feel I have earned the right to gripe. Bill says being a cranky bitch is part of my charm. I just don't have time for the nervous breakdown I deserve. As for the bright side, since I am totally not into negative vibes, Bill and I are excited about the football playoffs. Getting fired up for our annual Las Vegas Super Bowl trip. (The one I was unable to attend last year...can you believe it's been almost a year since that surreal diagnosis).

Started my cleaning project that I talked about last week. And by myself, I might add, since Bill is out of commission. (Sometimes I wonder...sounds like perfect timing to be sidelined with a back injury.) But I got one shed done and the garage attic. The back ordeal is kinda like his other disability...HEARING! Do you think men really have ears, or are those "things" attached to each side of their heads just detectors to pick up, recognize, and decode the word "SEX"? Does his back hurt now? OH BALLS!

Prayers out to the Arizona families who lost loved ones or who were injured in that senseless shooting over the weekend. God bless them.

Keep the faith!

RIDE, BABY, RIDE!

JANUARY 17, 2011

WOW...Where do I start? MRI results back on Bill. Doctor says it is a fracture, and it did happen during the fall on Christmas Day. Next step is a back brace for two to three months. Well, it was either that or surgery to pour cement in the crack! Sounds like paving a street, doesn't it? Somehow, we didn't feel real warm and fuzzy about the back surgery option. Sooo... Bill will be sporting an attractive brace for a while. I wonder whether Ralph Lauren makes one in blue?

I still have not heard anything about my blood work from last Thursday. Dr. Bevers gave me an A+ on the physical exam. Hopefully, the blood will reflect the same final score. I'm really nervous about it.

Still in the process of getting the portion of the floor put in that the washer messed up. Wouldn't you know that the Wilson-Art flooring we had has been discontinued. Our neighbor, Marvin, who is nice enough to help us out with this mess, found a guy in Killeen, TX who has it. So it is being shipped here.

Turning the BIG 60 on Friday. Looking forward to a wonderful celebration of life. This one means so much more to me.

"Who Who Are You?" We're having huge owl visitations. I just love owls. They are so beautiful, so regal, so powerfully in charge. Amazing, powerful, and graceful all at the same time. As we stare at each other intensely, I notice the beauty of their eyes. And the curiosity in them as to what I am thinking. In amazement, we practically talk to each other through our eyes. It is like a sign sent for how to start this year...to be more like it. I will fly into this year with hope, love, and determination to beat ovarian cancer. I will soar like my owl friends with the confidence of conquering my goals...to have conviction, courage, self-assurance, vigor, guts, and spunk.

We are approaching the one year anniversary of my surgery. The physical and mental devastation of what cancer can do! It has been a year of healing and coping, of meeting new friends, and appreciating the old ones. I plan on this being my last Monday Update for a while. After my birthday, we are planning a trip to Las Vegas for the Super Bowl and to see George Strait. From there, we come back home to gall bladder surgery along with an upper GI. It's okay...Dr. Bevers says it's like having a coupon. Two for the price of one! Probably a two night stay...because I'm sooo young! LOL! Isn't it funny how doctors say "Well, at your age..." instead of saying you are older than dirt and falling completely apart! Every time I'm at the store, I feel like I should grab the Depends and the Ensure just to be on the safe side!

So until next time, may all your dreams come true, and I will update you as soon as we have news from the February surgery.

RIDE, BABY, RIDE!

I received numerous emails from my friend Pat, one of my dearest friends. Pat and I worked together at the Kroger Co. where I was a customer service manager and wine steward. At this time, she was still working there as a pricing coordinator. I found this email especially touching:

JANUARY 17, 2011

You have been soaring with the Eagles, not just the Owls. You are way up there in my book, with all the courage, vigor, spunk, and self-assurance anyone would need. You had all this way before the cancer, and I know you will always have it....I love you my friend.

Patricia Humble

Chapter 13

PREPARING FOR THE FUTURE

FEBRUARY 14, 2011

OH MY! I'm Back!

Let's see...it's been a few weeks since our last little chat. Life has been good...if you overlook the little speed bumps. First of all, I want to thank all of my Monday Update fans. When I quit sending updates, I got so many emails about starting them back up that I felt like I was letting y'all down. It's not that I didn't have anything to say; it's just that I did not want to bore all of you.

So...my sixtieth birthday came and went without any unusual happenings. And only God knows when those will creep up and usually for a reason. Bill's back is still a challenge. He now has a cane and is moving about better. I think I could probably figure out another use for "those things"...WAYYYY to a woman's advantage. First of all...add a battery chamber!

Now...what you all have been waiting for...GEORGE STRAIT is...is...is...freaking awesome! The man should have to carry a license, one to bring women to their knees. Forget about him asking for sex...I'd be naked 24/7. We met up with his driver Allen before the concert and had steak dinner with the bands. George's and Reba's! Got to get on their buses and go backstage. So here comes the fun part. We had to clear four checkpoints without any badges. Leave it to us. Academy Award-winning performances! As you know, I get that talent from my dad. He pulls this BS every day.

Now, four checkpoints without any lies...I don't tell lies...period...no matter the outcome. So we were on our own from the word GO. Checkpoint one...Allen had his tag (his "I'm George's driver" tag), we had "We are nobody and we are going to die" tags...here and now! This gets good...and I ate it up. We walked right past the guard with Allen's tag. BS'ing about George. Worked like a charm.

Checkpoint two...two huge guys asking for ID. Allen shows his and I said, "Do you think this is still a surprise? George doesn't know we're here...does he?" Worked like a charm. Of course, I'd be a surprise to George, unless he remembers me from the ole college days in San Marcos. And then it's still no lie...he doesn't know I'm there. Just saying!

Checkpoint three...ten Nevada State troopers lined up. I just asked them for directions. They were so cute; Bill with his hurt back did the trick...Glad they weren't THE TEXAS BOYS...

would never have made it past the first one. Ate steak dinner with the bands. Awesome!

Checkpoint four...went past two women cops to get on the buses. Bill's back did the trick again. (Knew I brought him for something.) Allen and I were just laughing. The buses are more equipped than my house...damn. And cost more!

Did not get to meet George...but didn't care...had a blast! Concert lasted four hours...Life is good. Leave out the cancer and high school geometry and I'd do it again.

So as I turn sixty, I decided that the term "being too young" means anyone under twenty-one. No matter how mature, how smart you think you are...you are too young. Too old is when you are not happy, can't function, don't give a pooh pooh, and anyone over fifty acting or feeling that way. It's like trying to bounce a brick...ain't going to happen. No matter how hard you try, your ole butt ain't regaining altitude. Will Rogers said, "You know you are getting old if everything either dries up or leaks!" And...oh yeah...I forgot, I just bought a wine colored 2011 Jeep. Wrangler Sport! Watch out world...I'm roaming the streets...BUT I DON'T LIE!

I love you all...and to my dear friends, Dave and Terri, God is with you.

RIDE, BABY, RIDE!

FEBRUARY 21, 2011

Feels so good to be back in the saddle again.

I must start with Dad's latest escapade. Took him for one of his famous haircut adventures. You know most old retired people work only part-time at being an ass...Dad works full-time at being a complete ass and pain in the patootie! No rest for the weary when he is on his mission of making all miserable. Didn't take him five minutes into the ride to start bitching about how far it is to his barber. I told him I had a solution...but I'm almost positive it's illegal! I would call this whole experience PMS. Not what you're thinking. But PMS...pretty much sucks! Even taking him in my new jeep didn't help...it PMS'ed!

And if I'm not getting the treatment from Dad, Bill has to throw in his two cents worth. And believe me, it's not worth even two cents. Even with a bad back, the man can totally disappear off this planet without a trace! I have decided to invent another apparatus. A pager that you can shove up, oh I mean insert into, your husband's ass, and push an alarm button that goes off either to locate him or the TV remote (since they are usually together...attached at the hip)! Even our male dog (Moochie) hangs out with him. I could literally find both of them at once and the remote. It's like old men with bad backs bonding. Our female lab (Starr) has picked up on this testosterone BS and hangs with Mom...smart girl!

But I would like to say that things have been really good in Fulshear. Beautiful weather the last few days. Getting ready for the trail riders to mosey through town, cutting back our roses, and enjoying that cute little new jeep of mine. (Oh, by the way, I named her "Mame" after the movie *Auntie Mame*.) She is cherry-wine pearl. That's the color they had her listed as when we bought her. Been reading out in the hammock every day that the wind doesn't take me to the next county, and have had family and friends over to help celebrate life! Can't wait for it to get warmer. The pool is so inviting.

Thanks for all the emails full of support and encouragement. And for all the prayers. Next blood work is not until April 13th, so I'll be in panic mode the first weeks in April. No major problems that I notice. Certainly no problem pooping...as usual. The stomach pains have all but quit. Don't know what it was or what happened, but I'm not complaining. I guess I got tired of pulling up my "big girl panties"...I think the elastic was wearing out, and they were beginning to get holes in the crotch! (Which may not be a bad thing...just saying!)

RIDE, BABY, RIDE!

FEBRUARY 28, 2011

Hope everyone is having a great Monday! Not much going on here in Fulshear. Just enjoying a beautiful day. Planted some flowers in the front bed and did a little mowing for Bill. Even though it's a riding mower, it still hurts his back.

Had an x-ray of my right thumb. It has been bothering me for months. Thought I had broken it. Turns out that I have something called osteoarthritis. It could be caused by gout, which in turn could have been caused by an excess of uric acid, which in turn could have been triggered by chemotherapy. Oh well, that's the least of my worries. One thing I've learned over the past year is never say, "How could it get any worse?" Just grin and "Fight Like A Girl!"

Does anyone remember the Nancy Drew mysteries? I know growing up I read them all. Well, the little sleuth has stayed with me through the decades. I had to play amateur detective to figure out an interesting little case out here on the farm: The Mystery of the Hurles Pick-Up Truck. It looked like we were descended on by a flock of birds suffering from bowel disorders. Poop was everywhere. The windshield, the hood, the side mirrors, and the doors! Holy crap, Batman! So being of sound mind (I think) and not so sound body...I hid in the bushes next to the truck. In full camouflage! Took my glass of wine and a couple of cheese crackers. Hey...you never know how long it takes to solve a mystery. Anyway, I was there all of ten seconds when Daddy Cardinal flies up and proceeds to admire himself in the mirrors. Then he goes and does some kind of ritual dance on the hood. (Man, if Bill would court me like that, he might get a lot luckier!) The poor bird is in love with himself. It's a shame he was just s**t out of luck! The female was sitting in the bush next to me, and I do believe she's going to file for divorce on grounds of insanity. Even the mockingbirds watch him from the roof. It's amazing what you learn while incognito. Oh well, mystery solved. Now what do we do with psycho bird?

We're going to the rodeo on Saturday. Hope Bill doesn't have too much trouble with his back. We always enjoy our days out at the livestock show and rodeo. If Bill becomes too much of a pain in the ass, I'll just drop him off at the First Aid station with a couple of beers and have the docs take care of him while I go shopping and sightseeing. You know...cowboy hiney watching—one of my favorite rodeo hobbies!

RIDE, BABY, RIDE!

Chapter 14

YOU ARE BEAUTIFUL

MARCH 21, 2011

HUSBAND FOR SALE OR RENT! Comes equipped with cane, splints, bandages, stitches, prescription drugs, hearing aids (batteries not included), and I'll even throw in a bottle of Viagra, if it will help! Yes...he's done it again! Ovarian cancer is a breeze compared to having Bill around. This time his bad leg gave out as he was getting out of the shower. (No I did not push him...although a thought for later on.) Okay...Picture this...Leilani scraping a wet, buck-naked man off the bathroom tile. (I know...that is not too far-fetched!) Not to mention the added effect of scattered blood. Looked like a scene out of a movie. Not sure if it's a comedy or a drama. Bill is fine. So glad he did not reinjure his back. Did get four stitches in his right thumb and crushed his knuckle. We're waiting to see whether he needs surgery.

Hope all is well with all of you. Spring is in the air, and it's the time of year to start thinking about some critical subjects. First priority is my bluebonnets, which are not so much of an issue this year since Bill can't mow because of his back. Have you ever heard a bluebonnet as it breathes a sigh of relief? I can just feel their enthusiasm.

Aah...and of course, pool time! For men, this is no biggie, but for women, it's major. Which swimsuit looks best on a body that has been in hibernation all winter? And OMG, the holiday meals! Just how pale can skin turn in just a few months? Egad!

And the six letter word...SNAKES! The most disgusting creatures on the face of the planet. The only good one is a dead one. Whenever Lani or I let out a scream and yell, "Get the gun!" Bill takes off to the shed for the hoe and proceeds to decapitate it.

A new doctor experience...the dermatologist visit. Do you guys remember mixing the iodine and baby oil to get the Fab-tan? The Coppertone girl who showed her ass on every billboard in town has nothing on me. I walk in the office and the doctor says take off all your clothes! What is it with these men? I used to get dinner and wine before we got to that. Anyway, he checks for spots all over, including a freckle I have down near my "who-ha"! The man gets a magnifying glass out to look at it. I told him only two men in the world were allowed to do that...Bill and George Strait! Gee, even Dr. Bevers and Dr. Cook didn't take out a mag-glass! Add one more to the list of who has seen the ole cooter!

Have a great spring and enjoy the beauty of Nature at her best. Thinking of you all.

RIDE, BABY, RIDE!

MARCH 28, 2011

The Lord sure works in mysterious ways. Every day is a blessing, but some days are a real challenge compared to others. I'm beginning to think that ovarian cancer was a test to see how strong I am. The challenge now is skin cancer. The place on my nose (next to my right eye) came back positive for basal cell carcinoma. It will be removed by Mohs procedure on April 6th. The doctor said I'll be able to show off a few stitches for a couple of weeks. All I said was "Don't tinkle on my head, and then tell me it was raining!" At least Doctors Bevers and Cook's "900" stitches and staples were out of sight...but believe me, never out of mind!

Bill and I counted up that we have seven doctors' appointments in the next two weeks between us. Bill's leg, Bill's ear, Bill's thumb, and last, but not by any means least, one for Bill's bottom. Yes, time for the ole colonoscopy. The pain in the ass will have a pain in the ass! Abracadabra! (which means, I create as I speak). So, abracadabra, I wish to create...no more doctor appointments!

Our paint horse, Bud, developed an eye ulcer that we have been treating for two weeks. He is such a good boy and has been tolerating Lani and me dispensing his medicine in his eye—a lot better patient than the other two males who walk on two legs. Oh, and Lani and I have discovered that horses get wedges too! Really...no pooh pooh...their tail gets caught in undisclosed places. See, one can learn a lot being around horses!

Where there is smoke, there's dinner! And grilling at the Hurles' casa really gears up in the spring. The day we decided to grill steaks, Mother Nature decided to water the plants. So we brought the steaks inside and grilled them on the Jenn-Air. To make a long story short, the smoke detectors went off, which set the dogs off, which set the horses off, which set me off, which set the grill off, which set the smoke alarms off! Get the picture? Good. It was a zoo! Now, are you ready for this? Bill says, "What's all that noise?" Funeral arrangements are pending!

Pool is warming up a little each day. Soon it will be time for the "BIG SPLASH." Although I have been known to create a few big splashes in my time, this one will be a thunderous explosion of joy! Back to poolside cocktails, music, men in their cute little swim trunks or no swim trunks (even better, but of course that would have to be after we drugged Dad and got him to bed), and the wonderful warmth of the sunshine.

So my friends, love yourself...you are beautiful. As you start each morning, thank God for its beauty and say to yourself, "Self, I love you. I am beautiful too." Be competitive with life. Show the strength that is in you through the rough times. Believe me; I know how difficult times can be, but your attitude will make it better. Love, live, laugh, and enjoy.

RIDE, BABY, RIDE!

Chapter 15

LIFE'S FUNNIES HELP

APRIL 4, 2011

COWGIRL UP! (That's rodeo lingo for "Get your butt on the horse and go!")

Busy couple of weeks ahead. Most of it will not be pleasant, but hopefully, time will fly by and it will all be over soon, and we can move on. Mohs procedure to be done on Wednesday. Then the nerve-racking ordeal of waiting for CA-125 results from blood work. Just keep the prayers coming for negative cancer readings. Of course, waiting is always the worst part of anything.

Today is my youngest son Dusty's birthday. He is twenty-seven. He was kind enough to come over yesterday and cut his mother's hair...along with the grass. At least I was first in line. Happy Birthday, Dusty!

Lani and I went out Thursday for a girls' day. She had a dental appointment that morning, and then we ran a few errands, and then to lunch at P.F. Chang's in Highland Village. We had a great time, good food, and of course, outstanding wine. Left there and went to the mall and then off to Buffalo Wild Wings for a brew before we headed home. So we thought! As we were getting out of the car, we were discussing a movie when Leilani locked the keys in the Jeep. Lani was laughing her ass off. There is a reason why the Good Lord informed me to get the rag top instead of the hard top. (Can you imagine me turning down anything hard?) Lani proceeded to unzip the back side window and I gave her a boost. Okay, she was half-in and half-out with her derriere stuck up in the air. We were both laughing so hard that she said she was about to tinkle in her pants. She didn't...I DID! True tales of ER...emergency release!

When we got in the Jeep, I removed my pants and we drove to Kohl's where Lani jumped out and bought me a pair of jeans and underwear. If the parking lot security cameras were working, the guards got an eyeful. With me buck-naked from the waist down, we left Kohl's and drove back to Buffalo Wild Wings. I was in the process of getting dressed while Lani was warning me of people walking up on the passenger side. We both lost it again. I was now driving home, naked from the waist down, daring Lani to open her mouth when she says, "Wouldn't it be funny if you got stopped by the cops?" If you pass a thirty-two year old hitchhiking to get home...IGNORE HER!

I'd like to close by saying that people see things in you that you don't see in yourself. God calls those people friends. Listen to them. It might surprise you what you hear. My minister, Dave Peterson, went through brain surgery several months ago. He was back preaching after one month. I know how tough it must be to get up in front of the congregation on Sundays for three sermons while trying to balance yourself. Dave and his wife have been so supportive of me over the last year, so I'd just like to say to Dave, "When I grow up, I want to be just like you!"

Have a great week....I love you all!

RIDE, BABY, RIDE!

As usual, Terri and Dave Peterson continued to be my cheerleaders to publish the book as this response shows:

APRIL 4, 2011,

Leilani, you totally lighten up my life! This is so hilarious. I hope, hope, hope the book gets published. When I told Dave, he said, "Well, it SHOULD be published!" You are so darn much fun. Thanks for your kind comments about vertigo Dave! Okay, today, right now, praying for good test results. Feels like it never ends, doesn't it? Anji would agree!!!

Love ya,

Terri

APRIL 11, 2011

Picasso would be proud! My body feels like one of his paintings, a mosaic, a 3,000-piece jigsaw puzzle being put together by a four year old! Nothing matches or fits. Absolutely nothing is where it's supposed to be. "Masterpiece" my ass! Oh yeah, speaking of which, I've been working on gaining weight and I have managed ten pounds. So my ass is finally getting some form back. Although when your butt size grows, so does your pant size! Bill says it's just an excuse for me to go shopping. You know...he's getting pretty smart on my schemes to get to the mall. I did get in the pool Saturday and Sunday. It was so wonderful! Could not get my face wet (that's an upcoming story), but I did exercise and did laps with head up.

Had the Mohs procedure done on the basal cell carcinoma last Wednesday. All went well. It looks like someone high-fived my right eye! Seven stitches and a black eye in tow, but all of the cancer cells were removed after two scrapes. Did not need the pain pills, but I did take the antibiotics, which caused massive runs to the bathroom...but hey, Leilani's my name and pooping's my game!

Dad had another dental experience. He had to have another tooth pulled. I swear his teeth have to be petrified rock. They could be classified as fossils from pre-World War I days. Brought him home and he had set his thermostat on 80 degrees heat. It was like walking into the jungle at the equator. I envisioned little cannibals jumping out naked with forks and knives waving in their tiny little hands and screaming, "Grab the one with no teeth!"

Had blood work done last Tuesday for the CA-125 test. Have not heard the results, but I see Dr. Bevers on Wednesday for my three month physical. I figure "Curiosity killed the cat." I dare not call them. They are either good and they are waiting to tell me at my appointment, or they are not so good, and he wants to tell me in person...or as of Friday, they had not received the results and will call me soon. Please pray for great results. I've been having my usual long conversations with Jesus because I am a nervous wreck!

We sent income tax stuff in to Uncle Sam. Hard to believe it has been one whole year since that. But Bill and I did get confirmation on our season tickets for the Houston Texans. So we are now proud owners of four seats. Now...if we can just get the NFL on the ball and get the football season to start without a shutdown. Between our government and the NFL, I seriously want to know, "What is wrong with these people?"

Enjoy each day my friends...I love you all. Hugs!

RIDE, BABY, RIDE!

APRIL 18, 2011

Sorry for the late update today. Lani had a dentist appointment this morning.

Wanted to start off by letting everyone know that the CA-125 results came out well, and so did the pelvic and rectal exams. (As "well" as one can be with a finger extended up an orifice!) No signs of cancer. Will have a CT scan next week to make sure everything is okay inside too. So thank you for all your prayers and keep them coming.

I know everyone is ready for another Bill adventure. The man lost the end-piece to his right hearing aid...the little rubber tip that goes on the end of the hearing piece. He is telling me he thinks it's stuck down in his ear and he can't get it out. He is telling me this information on the way to the vet to get the dogs their shots. So I sat his ass on the examining table and had the vet look in his ear while she looked in the dogs'. Would like to report it was not there. Moochie and Starr were excited that Daddy had to see the doctor too.

What is 5'6" tall, uses a walker, and picks locks? GUESS! So we have changed Dad's name from Magoo to Houdini. We cannot figure out how he does it. We will lock the door, and the next thing you know, he's standing right beside you. Scares the crap out of ya! I guess I'll get in my camos again and hide in the bushes (which I'm getting very good at) with my binoculars to see his technique. I've gone through his pockets to see what could possibly pick the lock. Breath mints, lollipops, toothpicks, Kleenex, Band-Aids, and Rolaids. Mystery is still in progress!

We receive fresh eggs from our neighbors' hens about once a week. This week, we were given a dozen, and you could not close the lid to the carton. Seriously, two eggs were huge. That poor hen deserved a C-Section. Super-hen has been renamed MOTHER CLUCKER!

Thanks for all the great leads on book publishers. I did get in and meet the secretary to the President of M.D. Anderson Cancer Hospital. Hopefully, we can get some backing or at least get a foot in the door. Maybe the word will get out and we can help some really great people who need it.

FYI...can you sell people on eBay? Love you all!

RIDE, BABY, RIDE!

By this point, I was seriously thinking about the idea of turning these emails into a book. My brother, Delmore, and my minister Dave Peterson especially encouraged me as I began to think about the project in earnest now that I thought I was near the end of my cancer journey. The idea that my own experiences—the pain of ovarian cancer and the way I used humor to work through it—could inspire others was becoming a mission for me. Through her blog, I met author Chris Bledy.[1] She had already written a book about ovarian cancer, and when I mentioned how people were telling me I should turn my emails into a book, she told me she had been coached through the book writing process by Patrick Snow.[2] Once I was put in touch with

1 You can find out more about Chris Bledy and her book, Beating Ovarian Cancer: How to Overcome the Odds and Reclaim Your Life at www.beatingovariancancer. com

2 Patrick Snow is a publishing coach and an international best-selling author. You can visit him at www.PatrickSnow.com

Patrick Snow, I told him how I had been encouraged to put this book together and he helped me head in the right direction, walking me through the publishing process.

APRIL 25, 2011

How old is old? I started exercising in the pool again. Finally! The water is now hovering in the upper-eighties and feels great. Been doing thirty laps a day along with some water aerobics. But after laying off all winter, not only does the water feel eighty, but so does Leilani!

Is old when you go to the doctor and you realize that you have to pay someone to look at you naked? I think I'll enjoy the next office visit so much that I'll make sure they take their time and I get my money's worth! It's like feeling bad in the morning without partying the night before. Egad!

Hope everyone had a wonderful Easter holiday. Bill and I slipped away to the Good Friday service. And Saturday was a workday. Lots of mowing, laundry, cleaning, washing the vehicles, and of course, a snooze in the hammock. Sunday was family day. Poor Dad was having a hard time, but having everyone over seemed to perk him up.

I'm not looking forward to tomorrow...CT scan time again. Fasting, IV with dye, drinking the pooh-pooh juice forced on you by the army of "scrub people." They run around in their array of different colored pant sets giving orders at 7 a.m. Which is very annoying since you didn't get much sleep, no coffee, and are hungry! And it's always fun to wear the hospital gown. Toga party! Great fun mooning people in the wee morning hours. You think I won't? Why do you have to wear a gown anyway? It's like they think you are going to smuggle something in under your clothes. Food maybe! Could wear my camo scrubs and hide in the broom closet...or naked and hide in the broom closet...no, the damn janitor would recognize me!

And I'm not a "we"...I'm an "I." We are not in a pissy mood this morning...I am in a pissy mood this morning! We did not fast last night...I starved myself to death last night! The nurses drive me crazy with that "we" stuff. So, wish we well...I mean me well, and pray for a negative CT scan!

Hope everyone has an incredible week. And for those of you not in Texas, you may not know this, but we need RAIN. Please pray for rain! If you google our home from space, you will see me out doing a rain dance...who knows, in camo scrubs, or hospital gown, or naked! No we want rain, not to scare it off. Love you all.

RIDE, BABY, RIDE!

Chapter 16

HELPING OTHERS HELP YOU

MAY 2, 2011

First of all, great news about getting Bin Laden and celebrating the asshole's demise! Who better to punish him than our Lord? Wow...wouldn't want to be in his flip-flops right now...would you?

To start out, I need a group hug. I had a small setback last Wednesday with the CT scan results. Dr. Bevers called me on Wednesday evening to tell me there was a small spot somewhere between the rectal "something" and my vagina. He ordered an ultrasound for my lower abdomen and pelvic area. It will take place this Wednesday at 8:30 a.m. Hopefully, it is nothing and we can continue on our quest to beat this thing. But you know me..."my bad"...I cheated on my CT scan. Well, I had to have my chocolate truffles Folgers coffee! I know they said to fast... but I had to have that morning java! So maybe that did something to the scan. I hope. Praying whatever it is will have disappeared by Wednesday.

We've been having some Nature encounters lately. First of all, I was reading my book in the hammock when a ladybug came for a visit. She landed on my hand and then strolled to my book and then back. Must have been on a mission—girls' day out or something. Maybe needed new pairs of shoes (three pairs to be exact). I informed her of some interesting facts that I knew about her species...like she really isn't a bug. I think that boosted her confidence. Next thing I knew, she had a friend join her. Literally! Did you know that ladybugs do it doggy style? Imagine that with six legs! I think my next Nature discussion will be with a rose. I don't think they are into the porn thing.

The next visit was by a baby green lizard. Actually an Anole (although some call it a chameleon, it's not). He was desperately trying to make it from a post to a hanging basket. His jumps were in vain...he always fell a little short. Well, I know how that feels so I helped him a bit. I pushed the basket a little closer to him. So on his third try...Bingo!...he made it. He was so proud of himself, and Bill and I were so proud of ourselves. It just takes such a little thing to make someone feel good. I wish each of us would try doing that just once a day. What a difference it would make in this world.

Everyone is asking about Bill. He's still having his right leg pain. He went to a pain management doctor. (We did not know they even existed!) He sent Bill to a rehab place for therapy. I told him just to get his ass in the swimming pool and I would show him some exercises to do. He seems to be walking better after just three days of pool "honey-do's."

With all the weird things happening on this planet—weather, war, earthquakes, etc.—I am focused on a new project. Designing an underground cellar ready for anything, equipped with wine, bedding, food, emergency kit, and George Strait picture on the wall. The trick would be to get Bill to hear the emergency siren. And to get Dad in the ground in time, trying to tootle over with his walker. We would probably all be blown to smithereens waiting for him and Bill. I could get the horses and dogs in quicker!

Wish me luck....Prayers are really needed now....Keep them coming. I love you all. Hugs!

RIDE, BABY, RIDE!

MAY 9, 2011

This update has to begin with the unforgettable ultrasound experience I had last week. It is a good thing that all turned out okay because the technique they use is right up there with water boarding! The CIA has nothing on the St. Luke's crew. They used a vaginal wand! Yes, I said a vaginal wand! I only had one last thought as I saw it disappear...I am not married to the Jolly Green Giant or Paul Bunyan! Like my cousin Norma said, "He must have big feet!" OMG...I told the tech that there is not enough K-Y Jelly in the world to insert that thing. I was wrong! Suggestion to Dr. Bevers: Order one that at least glows in the dark, vibrates, and is warm! Last thing I remember saying to myself was "Self, think happy thoughts." Yeah right. Open wide and say, "OUCH!" I get to go through it again in six weeks. I'm working on vaginal stretching exercises. Lucky Bill!

The mockingbirds have decided to build a nest in the lime tree right outside our bedroom window. So every morning, I wake up to two little eyes staring at me. I have been breaking up pecan pieces for her and her mate and they love it. Now it is expected every day, and believe me, they are there waiting. But poor Starr and Moochie will have to drag out their protective gear again. And get ready for the bombardments.

Bill has an appointment with the urologist on Wednesday to see whether the pain in his right leg might be related to a prostate problem. We just can't seem to pinpoint the problem.

Dad turns ninety-seven on Wednesday, May 11th. He is really slowing down now, a lot weaker and more confused. But when my kids were here on Mother's Day, he came out and sat by the pool to watch the swimming activities and listen to the Astros game. And even at ninety-seven, men never cease to amaze me. He was really watching all the young ladies in their bikinis.

Enjoy your week, my friends. I love you all and thanks for all the continuous prayers.

RIDE, BABY, RIDE!

MAY 16, 2011

I have now added a new talent to the many I have acquired since my "total life" wake up call! If anyone is in the market for a urine measurer, let me know. It's so nice to know you can excel in such interesting tasks. Bill has to go through a battery of tests for his prostate and bladder exams. We had to measure his intake of liquids and the output of urine. This test lasted for twenty-four hours, the longest twenty-four of my life. It really is a test of agility for our male friends. I decided you have to be ambidextrous. If you are right-handed, do you hold the measuring cup with your right hand and your appendage with the left, or the other way around? And add Bill's balance problem to the right leg pain and you had a real circus. And NO...I did not offer to hold either one! I handled the paperwork and the measuring. Needless to say, Bill kept me amused all day. If you see a slightly used measuring cup on eBay...just pass!

Well, Dad made it to his ninety-seventh birthday. Magoo actually behaved himself at the country club. And we had a gathering over here yesterday. Dusty (my youngest) did the BBQ, and Dad endured hours of loud '60s music and pool volleyball. Will wonders never cease? The end must be near because he would have protested the loudness in the past.

Mother Mock has four little blue eggs in her nest and was not at all thrilled about the '60s music either. We moved the pit away from her lime tree so we could avoid the fussing and her "Go to Hell!" stares. The looks could have cooked the chickens thcmselves! But she hung in there like all good moms. She was persistent and prevailed over the human activities. Moochie and Starr still won't go near her...even with their combat gear on.

As far as me...I'm great! Of course, relieved for another few months until the next checkup is due. Grateful for another beautiful day. I had lunch with my cousins, Sandra and Beckye, at PF Chang's on Thursday. Had a blast. And had an early dinner with our friends Linda and David on Saturday at Collina's, which by the way has the best pizza in town.

I keep the blinds open all night, so I can see the stars at night and the amazing sunrises in the mornings, and see Mom Mock stretching her wings, the cardinal family at the bird feeder, an occasional cottontail feeding, and the slight ripples of the pool water being rocked by the gentle breeze. Yes, lucky to be alive. So think FROG (Forever Rely On GOD). He is full of Heavenly Hugs!

RIDE, BABY, RIDE!

MAY 31, 2011

I hope everyone had a wonderful Memorial Day weekend. Here in the Houston area, it was beautiful. But I know that many had tragedies to overcome: the tornadoes that hit and the fighting all over the world that has intensified. But when I saw young children running to their parents' arms who were back from Iraq and Afghanistan, I couldn't help thinking, "That is what God wants us to do with Him." Embrace Him and hold on tight in these troubled times.

In the past few weeks, I have reflected on what I think God has been communicating to me. He wants me to talk about Him. To tell others that there is no limit to what you can accomplish. Things do not happen by coincidence. It's part of a plan. I have said before that I feel we meet people in our lives because it is part of a plan. And trying to publish this book is a plan. One to help others grow and overcome illness and negative thoughts and ways. Thoughts just pop up in my mind. Kinda like one of those children's pop up picture books. Where the thoughts come from used to be a mystery to me. Now I know—God is feeding me those thoughts and not giving up on me.

I have noticed that many of you begin or end your emails with Live, Love, Laugh, Light, Listen...all of these should be part of our everyday life. The Divine pop-up. Passing the word not to forget what we are here for...our purpose.

I have talked to many wonderful people in trying to write my book. I have talked with the secretary of the President of M.D. Anderson, I have talked with the CEO of CanCare (she and her husband are childhood friends of mine), and many who have written books on hope, love, and humor. But the ones who give me the main support are all of you. Friends help friends succeed...it works both ways. So channeling my hopes and dreams for others, and of course, for a cure for the ugly thing called cancer, I have picked up the ole pencil to let you know how I really feel.

I have great news from Bill's test results. No cancer, just an extremely large prostate that will be taken care of through a sound wave procedure. But that scope procedure they did on him was a real trip! Talk about a pop-up story! His leg pain is better, I guess because I have dumped his ass in the pool every day to do his leg exercises. Now he says I not only nag him around the house, but I nag him in the water too. A woman's work is never done.

So my friends...help a neighbor and love each other. A hug for each of you. Have a great week. (Can't believe it is June already). My next ultrasound of the "who-ha" is June 15th...I'll be in touch.

RIDE, BABY, RIDE!

Chapter 17

HURRY UP AND WAIT

JUNE 6, 2011

Guess what? Yes, eliminate pregnancy and all that OMG stuff cause there ain't no way that's happening with all the reproduction parts missing from the mid-section. No, it's another porch adventure. This time we add a new equation to the life and times of Magoo (Dad). His dog Lilly has joined him in the ranks of "His elevator skips floors," "His chain is missing links," "His door doesn't close all the way," etc. I think the dog has inherited through osmosis Dad's malfunctioning brain waves. There is a rabbit family that lives under Dad's porch steps. The rabbits drive Lilly nuts. She is constantly putting her little nose in the rabbit hole. Okay, picture this...Dad and dog sticking noses in the rabbit hole. All we could see were two butts in the air. Hate to admit it, but Lilly's is a lot cuter! Just saying! All of a sudden, the rabbit runs out another hole on the other side. Now I know that Bugs thought it was bad enough to have to look at the nose of a dachshund, but when a human starts sticking his ninety-seven year old proboscis where it doesn't belong, it's a whole different ballgame! Lilly runs after Bugs, knocking Dad backward on his ass. The rest of the bunny family emerges and heads for the horse field; now, Lilly doesn't know whether she is coming or going. And Magoo is trying to get up, completely tangled up in his robe. Bill and I are doubled over in laughter. And once again, I am asking myself the age ole question..."Why me, Lord?"

Couldn't sleep the other night. Just one of those toss-and-turn type nights where you think of everything but can't remember pooh pooh the next morning. I went out on the porch and was overwhelmed by the night sky. It was beautiful. It looked like one huge "Connect the Dots." The stars just dusted the sky like snowflakes. It was amazing. Right away, you notice that some shine brighter than others. It's like you want to go put a battery in the dim ones to help them brighten up. Just think if you could do that to people. Help the ones who need a little boost to brighten up by reaching out and touching them in some way. Catch some falling ones and return them to their beautiful place among the others. I think that's the way angels work. Like being touched by an angel. That's the way I felt revived after the blow that I have ovarian cancer. My family and friends were and are my angels. They helped me return to my place where I needed to be. And for that, I am so grateful. BELIEVE!

Have a wonderful week full of bright stars!

RIDE, BABY, RIDE!

I continued to have people insist I write a book, including my cousin Sandra's significant other, Shel Mitelman:

JUNE 6, 2011

Hi L:

Sandra just forwarded your Monday update, and I have to tell you that you missed your calling—You should have been an author; you're a very expressive, humorous, and very talented writer.

People always say to me…"I can't draw a straight line with a ruler" to which I reply "Your talents lie elsewhere"…and that's You baby, you!

Really glad you're doing well. Keep it up. My best to Bill and Oved. Would love to be included on your email updates.

Happy to be one of your angels.

Cheers!

Shel

JUNE 13, 2011

I've always been told that I could sell a spot to an Appaloosa horse. Well, hopefully this week, I can convince that ultrasound tech to find a better feeling instrument for the ole cooter! Yes, it's time once again for the vaginal ultrasound. No "holes" barred, so to speak. I will also have blood work done that day, and then an appointment with Dr. Bevers on the following

Monday. So the update will be late next week. Please continue to pray for wonderful negative results. Bill has two tests tomorrow for his leg pain. Maybe I should just go ahead and confess that I kicked the bejeezers out of him while he slept one night! No really...poor guy has an MRI and a myelogram. Next week, he has some type of nerve test done on his leg. So count us as doctor bait for the next couple of weeks.

We went to the horse track Saturday with our friends Linda and David. It was Belmont time. Bill got lucky and hit a nice exacta, which will definitely give me a few trips to Chico's in the near future. I wore a fun lime green outfit I had bought there several weeks ago, and I know people thought I looked like a highlighter. I know one thing...you couldn't miss me.

A male cardinal was hanging around on our back porch. It was kinda going around in circles, so I went out to see whether I could help it. Poor thing acted like it had two left wings. Ya know, I've known people I thought had two left feet. Pretty much the same with this little guy. I helped him along, and finally, he took off flying. I guess he had accidentally run into the window. Probably was the same one who several months ago was trying to mate with himself in the truck mirror. I had a brief conversation with him and told him it's like going through chemotherapy. You feel sometimes like you have two left everything! Except of course "who-ha's." I don't think you can have two left ones of those.

I heard once that a stubborn friend walks behind you. An impatient friend walks ahead of you. But a true friend walks beside you. Thank you all for being true friends. Remember to listen to those God inspired thoughts...act on them and they will lead you in the right direction.

RIDE, BABY, RIDE!

JUNE 21, 2011

God said He would never give you anything that you couldn't handle...or something along that line. I think He made that statement without Dad in the equation! So I am opening with a Magoo moment. Dad decides to take a shower. He always announces his intentions because I need to make sure he gets in and out safely. It's part of our system. However, coming to the front door buck-naked while we have guests on our back porch is not part of our system. He opens the door and says he needs some help. This could be anything from "I can't find a bar of soap" to "I fell and there is blood all over the bathroom." Well, it was neither. I followed (without his walker) naked Magoo to his bathroom, and when we got there, he said he couldn't get the sprayer back on the holder! I needed scuba gear. There were two inches of water on the bathroom floor. Everything was drenched...even Lilly (his dachshund) who was stationed behind the bathroom door looking for a snorkel. The toilet bowl looked like a Jacuzzi. The vanity was a small pond. All we needed to do was add fish. Okay...do I look like Stanley Steemer...looking for alpaca poop to scoop? Or do I just need to go get the wet vac? I have renamed his bathroom Lake Magoo. Never install a shower massage in a handicap-equipped shower

stall for a ninety-seven year old. Hell, I don't know what was
worse...Lake Magoo or naked Magoo. OMG!

The other challenges God gave us this week were health-relat-
ed. Bill had all his tests run for his leg pain and still has one
more MRI of his neck to go before his final analysis. I, on the
other hand, was handed a real shocker. My CA-125 came back
a little high. Last time, it was a 6 and now it is a 16. Dr. Bevers wants to take it again in three weeks. So please pray that
we are not headed into round two. I just wish I could pick up
the binoculars and look into the wrong end and make all this
stuff look so far away instead of the way it's supposed to be and
bringing it closer.

But we have lots of friends and family support. Even the "couch
case" Magoo was part of the pep squad. Lani and I had lunch
with one of my dear girlfriends Pat. I had dinner and drinks
at Ray's with two of my dear friends—and I might add, my
support team—Benny and Carol. And Bill and I had dinner
with our ole friends Linda and David on Saturday. We also
went to the Astros game last Wednesday, thanks to our wonderful doctor and friend, Dr. Cook. I even got Angel Sanchez's
autograph. (He is the Astros shortstop.) Although he is not a
"shortstop," he's a "tallstop," and a total cutie pie.

So as I have said all along. The support you all give is amazing and it keeps us going. Keep the prayers coming....We need
every one of you.

RIDE, BABY, RIDE!

June 27, 2011

Have you ever wanted to pull your hair out completely? Thank goodness I have three wigs stored up for reserves. In our infinite wisdom, Bill and I decided to convert the garage into a little apartment. So that on occasions, the kids, friends, or relatives can stay the night in privacy and comfort. In a way, it is very timely because I need a mind-blowing project to keep my little brain busy. So I plugged in Dean Martin and George Strait and set to work on my plans for the garage. DO NOT, under any circumstances, ask your husband for advice on remodeling. I have come to the conclusion that he will put me in my urn faster than the dreaded cancer. Where are the minds of men located? Never mind—I know the answer to that, and that's exactly why his recommendations are ridiculous.

Has anyone ever had to poop while enjoying a wonderful day in the pool? With my butt on a float, a wine in tow, the dumb ass Astros on the TV in the saloon, and the weather perfect. And then the ole colon (or what's left of it), decides it time to empty. Now...that's not my dilemma. My problem, as I'm sure for women in general, is how do you get a wet bathing suit back up after doing the task? I was trying to remember back as a kid just exactly what my technique was. You would think as an ex-AAU swimmer, I would have this down to a tee. Maybe I didn't poop as a kid during a swim meet. WWEWD? (What Would Esther Williams Do?) So being the educated woman I am...I changed into a dry suit! Ya know I really feel sorry for my guardian angel. I hope the good Lord didn't assign me a trainee—one who can't fly and toot its flute at the same time! Or not as sharp as its harp! Oh well...it helped me get through the poop-and-suit crisis.

There is absolutely no way to describe the feelings of waiting out three weeks until the next blood work. Three more weeks of tossing and turning at night, getting up in the middle of the night and star gazing. And wondering every waking moment what's in store for the rest of this year. Every little pain puts me in panic mode and asking the Lord to keep me strong; really, not for me, but for my family and friends and those ladies who are also on their journey of fighting ovarian cancer. God has surrounded me with a wonderful karma. A glow, an armor of strength that no one or nothing can penetrate.

So RIDE, BABY, RIDE!

Chapter 18

HOLDING ON TIGHT

JULY 4, 2011

What things make other things appear bigger than they really are? Binoculars, bifocals, a magnifying glass, microscopes, dreams, egos, and imaginations. Well, I'm trying to keep my imagination contained. And it seems to be running wild! It has been so hard to keep my mind busy during these two weeks of my CA-125 waiting period. The 4th of July is helping. Also kids over, remodeling the garage and keeping numerous men in line. I once heard that God needed help supervising so he created women. I believe it! Any mom can relate to that.

I've been in Home Depot about one too many times in the past few weeks…way too much testosterone in that place! It bounces off the damn walls. I just about want to show everyone what a menopausal bitch is.

I've spent a lot of time in the pool. I believe that poets like Keats and Lord Byron wanted us to read between the lines. But out on the float, I was observing the clouds. As a kid, I used to sit with my mom, and we would tell each other what we thought the shapes of the clouds looked like. I decided that God wants us to read between the clouds. It's amazing the shapes that show up between the clouds.

I even saw a few hawks and kites fly by. I don't mean a kite that kids fly, but a bird that is just awesome. It has wings like a stealth bomber, and it is smaller and sleeker than a hawk. When I grow up, I want to be a kite!

Happy 4th to all and enjoy the day. I always wondered what the name of Paul Revere's horse was. What an incredible animal it must have been. Looking it up, I found out the horse he rode was named Brown Beauty. But it wasn't his horse... he didn't even own a horse! But they both made history, both seeking to survive a mission of destiny. No flies on their asses! Sound familiar? God bless our troops and God bless America!

RIDE, BABY, RIDE!

JULY 11, 2011

News from Magooville! As you know, we are converting our garage into a livable space for visitors. And as you know, this is mainly a project to keep my mischievous little mind off of my blood work count. Well, Magoo (Dad) is convinced that there is a devious plot behind all of this hoopla going on with the garage. He's decided we are in cahoots to move his entire medical team to the new room to care for him because his demise is imminent! Our driveway is made up of small rocks and pebbles. Have you ever seen a ninety-seven year old man scale a twenty-foot wide drive with a walker? We have decided the walkers need to come with options like your car. Shocks, jack those babies up, and V1 motor.

The fun part, other than literally falling over with laughter, was watching him make it from his house to the driveway. He ventures out in 100-degree heat, fully clothed with PJ's and robe. Oh, and not just any robe…his heavy winter robe! He rounds the first turn, and of course, has to hurdle dogs, floats, rafts, suntan oil cans, and towels. By this time, the raffle pool is up to about $100.00. There were some who actually thought he wasn't going to make it! So we have convinced dear Dad that the new room is for the dogs. They have their own air/heat, bed, chairs, refrigerator, and doggy door for convenience…so they don't have to use the front door. Are you sitting? Magoo says, "Oh, okay." Somehow, I have lost total control of this situation!

Now the subject of green beans. I'm a freaking genius at green bean growing. So that tells you it must not be that complicated. But they just keep coming. I have no idea what I've done to deserve such a wholesome crop. I mean, my beanstalks are awesome. Even Jack would testify to this. Anyone want to meet a giant? Anyone need beans?

On a closing note: People ask me whether I am sad for what has happened to me. NO! Like I feel and have said before…all this happened for a reason. And if this had not happened to me, I would not have begun to write, I would not have met some of you, and I would not have gotten this close to Jesus. Everyone needs his or her guiding light, his or her superstar. Whoever or whatever your source of love and peace is...get closer to it. God doesn't want us to be sad. Even in trying times, don't be sad. Happy is the word! Be happy. You are loved. You are you, and I am still me. Whether I'm worried or carefree, whether I'm funny or serious, the Lord made me and I'm special and SO ARE YOU!

RIDE, BABY, RIDE!

JULY 18, 2011

I guess we will start by talking about my ass. Bill and I had lunch with our friend Ron who is with the Big Brothers Big Sisters organization. We met at the Post Oak Grill and had a wonderful visit. Anyway, the subject of my rear end came up when we were talking about gaining weight after chemo. Yes, I have found my posterior. It was lost for a while, but now, I realize it just ran away from home. She's back! But different— returned flat with no cheeks. It's hard to moon anyone with a flat ass! If this is a problem you share with me, just remember what Winston Churchill said, "Attitude is a little thing that makes a big difference." Isn't that a great quote? It applies to everything. So bottoms up!

It is amazing how much life reminds me of a ladder. We start at the bottom, on the first rung, and work our way up. As we grow, we step up to another rung. Now we are gaining courage, still too close to the ground to worry about a slip and a fall. Then the next step up, it starts to get a little scary. Better hold on a little tighter, but you are up high enough where you can start to see things better and reach for new things. So we gain more confidence. Then a foot slips off and we panic. So now we face a dilemma. Do we give up and fall, or do we fight to stay on the ladder? I will never give up! And I am holding on for dear life.

I received that dreaded phone call this morning from Dr. Bevers. My CA-125 spiked from sixteen to thirty-four. So my foot has slipped off the rung, but I am still enjoying the view. A PET scan and probably more chemotherapy are to be scheduled sometime this week. So I hope y'all are ready to go through round two with me. The reason these trembling hands can hold onto the ladder is because I have all of you to push my butt back up. (Maybe that's why it's so flat!) Thanks for being there, and keep the prayers coming. I love you all.

RIDE, BABY, RIDE!

The news that I had to go through a second round of chemotherapy resulted in many heartfelt responses like this one from a childhood friend and swimming buddy:

JULY 18, 2011

Leilani, I am sorry for the news but will remain faithful in my prayers for you. As a matter of fact, I will light a candle in every church we enter—we are in Paris on vacation right now. You will beat this cancer! I love you and thank you so much for the Monday updates. Your journey and insight have such an impact on so many people.

Love you,

Cindi (Hogan)

JULY 26, 2011

Radioactive glucose? Really? Let me tell you about a PET scan. Everything is stored in chrome containers. Chrome suitcases, to chrome cylinders, to chrome syringes, to Leilani's IV, to Leilani's body. The true meaning of "glow in the dark"! Lani said she was going to open the sewer lid and throw me in to go live with the Ninja Turtles—Leonardo, Raphael, Michelangelo, Donatello, and Leilani. Just hanging with the mutants. Kinda has a nice ring to it...doesn't it? Or I could drink water with E.T. just by sticking my index finger in a glass. I was picking up signals from satellites. I know now how Superman felt about his kryptonite...Geez!

Lani babysat Magoo (Granddad) during the procedure. She was on her cell phone in the kitchen talking to her good friend Sarah in Austin when IT happened! Magoo expelled gas. Not just any ripper, but THE ripper. Sarah asked, "What was that noise?" Lani was on the floor laughing. My son Dusty said it was a piece of poop honking for the right-of-way! Then the man goes missing! Probably blew himself to China! Couldn't find him anywhere. We could just imagine him on top of the

neighbor's bull, playing cowboy Magoo. Can just see the head-
lines now: "Ninety-Seven Year Old Man Escapes Caregiver and
Is Found Straddling One-Ton Bull." But...he doesn't have any
gas. Good thing for the bull.

I want you all to know that I am in good spirits after receiving
the PET scan results. It is just a speed bump in life's road. I understand the doctor at M.D. Anderson who puts the ports in is
a real trip. So this should be an interesting ordeal. And a good
Monday update story. Keep the prayers coming. Don't give up
on me, for I will never give up on myself unless Jesus tells me
Himself that it's Judgment Day. Every day is a blessed day.

RIDE, BABY, RIDE!

**The news that I would have to go through a second round
of chemo led to many, many well wishes, but I think I was
most surprised to receive the following email from someone
I didn't even know but who understood what I must be going through and took the time to reach out to me:**

THURSDAY, AUGUST 18, 2011

Hi Leilani,

Consider this a "you don't know me, but..." email....We have a
mutual friend of a friend who has been forwarding your emails
to me for a couple of years now. She says that your sense of
humor and attitude reminded her of me when I was going
through my little fight with Hodgkins 5 years ago.

Well, your recent news left me sitting speechless and staring at my computer. I suppose as part of the ever-growing Leilani Fan Club, I feel like we're old friends or something. Having been through the fight, I at least feel some sort of connection and have been rooting for you for a while now. So, on one hand, I want to join the rest of the world in shouting a hearty, "This SUCKS!" On the other hand, I have a sneaking feeling that you're going to go through this next ordeal in typical Leilani fashion. I pray for an outpouring of grace, peace, and strength for you like you've never experienced. And since I seem to know you so well, I'll also add this: I don't think you need to summon up your inner warrior, fighter, survivor, or whatever—I think just being Leilani will give you what you need to meet this next round head on.

Lots and lots of people out here praying for you. I'm one of them.

John (McGinley)

Chapter 19

MOVING ON

Is it possible that life can throw two curveballs back-to-back? Yes. And I'm living proof. As I begin my second journey of fighting for my life, I intend to keep my Monday email updates going. I feel now more than ever that I can encourage you and others to keep the faith. God always has challenges for us. Mine is not to give up on you. We are all here for a short time. Our adversities are numerous and have many different faces. We can conquer them together.

Within every being lies a little voice…your conscience. Your "go-to guy" who's supposed to guide you through rough times, challenging decisions, and the "should I, or should I not's" of life. It even has a hand in the "give ups, or don't give ups." Time will tell us whether we chose the right path. Some paths are good and some really stink! What it comes down to is that this is our decision to make. God wants us to love life and love each other. That's why encouragement is so important. Our determination not to give up is engraved in our souls. I encourage you to strive to reach where you thought impossible. Remember, nothing happens by coincidence. You are not alone. Believe in yourself!

Until next time, RIDE, BABY, RIDE!

I am here for you. Believe in yourself! And until next time, RIDE, BABY, RIDE!

Leilani Hurles

Information on

Ovarian Cancer's Signs and Symptoms

Ovarian Cancer can sneak up on you. To protect yourself, here are signs and symptoms to watch for:

- Back pain
- Indigestion, heartburn, nausea, or gas
- Abdominal swelling or discomfort ·
- Pelvic pain or cramping
- Bloating or a feeling of being full, even after a small meal
- Painful, frequent, or burning urination with no infection
- Diarrhea or constipation
- Loss of appetite, unexplained weight loss or gain
- Unusual fatigue
- Shortness of breath
- Abnormal vaginal bleeding or irregular periods
- Pain during intercourse

Please remember these signs and symptoms may be attributed to a number of conditions other than ovarian cancer. The most common tumor marker is a blood test called the CA125.

A PERSONAL NOTE:

I was diagnosed with stage 3 ovarian cancer. I have always been physically active and never thought about the few symptoms I had. I attributed my shortness of breath, feeling full at meals, and a pain in my groin area—that seemed to go down my right leg...mostly at night when lying down—to my age (getting ready to turn sixty) and post-menopausal "leftovers." Please check with your doctor if you are worried or unsure about any of the signs or conditions that could be ovarian cancer.

HELPFUL WEBSITES:

www.cancare.org

www.cancer.org

www.cancer.gov/help

www.mdanderson.org

www.ovarian.org

HELPFUL BOOKS:

Bledy, Chris. Beating *Ovarian Cancer: How to Overcome the Odds and Reclaim Your Life*. Lake Placid, NY: Aviva Publishing, 2008.

Montz, F.J., Robert E. Bristow, and Paula J. Anastasia. *A Guide to Survivorship for Women with Ovarian Cancer.* Baltimore, MD: John Hopkins University Press, 2005.

About the Author

Leilani Essary Hurles is a retired teacher and coach, mother, wife, author, and a stage three recurring ovarian cancer survivor. She has devoted the last year-and-a-half to uplifting spirits for those who just need a big hug.

Leilani has a B.S. degree in Education from the University of Houston. She currently resides with her husband, horses, and dogs in Fulshear, Texas. She hopes her book brings hope and laughs to all battling cancer or any other adversities in life.

She continues her weekly Monday email updates. If you would like to sign up for Leilani's updates, visit her at:

WWW.RIDEBABYRIDEBOOK.COM